The Science Spell

The Science Spell

Essays on
Why Science
Can Coexist
With Spirituality

ഔ

Chris Spark

Volume I of
Making Belief:
Essays Towards a Natural, Magical, Intelligent Faith

Cover Art by Guita Naeima
Cover Design by Immaculate Studios

ISBN: 978-1-7369107-0-2

Other titles by Chris Spark:

Of Geometry & Jesus:
Essays from Outside the Fishbowl of Western Culture
(Volume 2 of the *Making Belief* essay series)

Haiku Wisdom: 101 Daily Morsels for the Spirit

Advice for Me & Maybe You: Poems

This Dreaming World: Poems

The Trees Sing Hallelujah: Selected Poems

www.SparkWrites.com

To Dad & Mom,
for the science and the something beyond.

Contents

Introduction

"Knowledge of what is possible is the beginning of happiness."
—*George Santayana*

Smart people often listen to their hearts as they make their way through life. They follow a calling, fall in love, sacrifice for their children, or speak out for what's right. But when it comes to pondering the end of their lives, they often feel forced to listen to their brains. Yes, that brain says, you had some experiences that felt meaningful. But that's over now. Death is the end of everything. Ultimately, existence is meaningless.

Isn't that, our brain asks, the only sane conclusion?

Surely we can only believe in some sort of divinity by abandoning our intelligence. Isn't religion, or any form of spirituality, childish? Absurd stories at odds with common sense are something we grow out of. Are we to accept that mechanical rules govern our daily existence, but somehow don't apply in a realm we've never seen? Or that the randomness and injustice of the world are part of some invisible plan? Are we to make peace with a God who is either too cruel to deserve our affection or too good to be true? What's more, there are a thousand versions of this inanity. Which religion got its story right? Who wins?

No one, say those we turn to for more reasonable answers. There is no God. What Science offers instead is a unified, rational view of existence that squares with what everyone experiences every day. Scientists can be Canadian or Hungarian, Catholic or Hindu, but they all accept the evidence of their universal, human senses. They all use their universal, human logic to mine that evidence for the laws of nature. Laws we can count on. Laws that work. Religions start wars. But Science improves our crops, builds our computers, lights our homes, and carries us comfortably around the planet, unless you fly coach.

So which is it? Do you want a universe that cares? Or do you want a functioning brain? It seems to many we have to choose.

These essays beg to differ.

But not by questioning the truths of Science nor minimizing its contributions to humanity. The scientific approach has been hugely successful. It's given us iPhones, jets, air-conditioning, and chickens that can bench-press small cars. These essays respect the intelligence that made our amazing modern lives possible. They won't ask you to take leaps of faith or click your heels three times and wish away the truths our scientists have revealed.

In fact, these essays ask you to be even more scientific than mainstream Science is used to being. They push its critical probing further. They go places where our most educated and well-respected citizens generally don't. They ask questions that are usually ignored. What kind of information does Science really give us? How do scientists really go about their jobs? What can Science or its human servants really say about God—or whatever word we choose for some ultimate, comforting *something*.

It certainly seems as if scientists have peered into the farthest reaches of space and the smallest specks of matter and come up empty. *Seems*, though, is the operative word. These essays explore a paradox. The apparently obvious notion that the universe is impersonal, mechanical, and devoid of magic may itself be a kind of spell.

A Note on Essay Sequence

I've arranged these essays intuitively in an order that seemed right to me, but I also wanted each to be its own complete experience. So I invite you to read them singly or in whatever order they whisper or call to you.

I. The Science Fiction
How Scientific Are Scientists?

"I guess if everybody went crazy together, nobody would notice."
—*Cormac McCarthy*

Many intelligent people believe that Science is the ultimate authority on ultimate reality. The technology in our immediate reality makes a compelling case for this idea. The benefits of Science are the soundtrack of our lives: electricity, air-conditioning, iPhones, computers, cars, and flavor-resistant tomatoes. Surely the same group of smarties who brought us all these must also be experts on the deepest matters of all.

Science, after all, has a reputation for being the objective, unbiased appraisal of what is. It is, to many, simply the truth. Not the truth we might like to be the truth, but the real truth. And Science does not believe in God, gods, spirits, the spiritual, or any story that renders reality human.

Yes, says Science, there are unseen forces at work. But they are impersonal. Existence is mechanical and without meaning. Any other belief requires some kind of shenanigans—some agenda, some suspension of logic and disregard of facts. Science, we imagine, is the discipline that's invulnerable to these fallibilities—the one that stares unblinking at everything. Science, by its nature, is safeguarded against the monkey business of wishful thinking and hidden, all-too-human motives.

But Science has one annoying characteristic. It doesn't exist.

If it did, you would have heard of Prahlad Jani.

What Gets Swallowed

Prahlad Jani is an Indian holy man who claims to have lived without eating, drinking, or passing waste since 1940. In 2003, under the direction of Doctor Sudhir Shah at Sterling Hospital in Ahmedabad, India, a medical team observed Jani continuously for ten days in a sealed room. During this time the doctors reported that indeed Jani did not eat, drink, urinate, or defecate. Urine did appear to collect at times in his bladder but then disappeared, apparently reabsorbed by his bladder walls (something that's not supposed to happen).

In 2010, the Indian military got involved. Thirty-five researchers joined Dr. Shah under the authority of the Defense Institute of Physiology and Applied Science (DIPAS) to observe Jani for a longer period: fifteen days. In a repeat performance, Jani did not eat, drink, or pass waste. This time, according to Dr. Ilavaghazn, head of the DIPAS team, the 82-year-old Jani emerged not only in good shape, but—according to blood tests, hormone profiles, MRI's, and angiographs—healthier than someone half his age. Said Dr. Shah in an interview, "We are all scientifically educated and research-orientated doctors. We racked our brains and it was the greatest surprise of our [life]... As if a bomb had hit us. The complete history of science has to be written anew."

How long a human is supposed to be able to survive without food is up for some debate. Forty days is considered extreme. The verdict on going without water is clearer: about four days. Due to accumulation of toxic chemicals in the blood, lack of urination should also kill you after three or four days.

Whether Prahlad Jani has defied these beliefs and gone without food, water, or elimination since 1940 has not been settled. But if the Indian studies are valid, something of some degree of amazing is going on in his body. Something that could expand or shatter our fundamental notions of biology and of what a human is capable of. Something akin to the revolution in physics kicked off by Einstein when he proposed—absurdly and correctly—that motion is the same as the stuff that's *in* motion (mass is energy—or in math talk, $E=mc^2$).

Scientists are, theoretically, humble before the facts they meet. You'll hear this humility trumpeted over and over by prominent scientists from Neil DeGrasse Tyson to Bill Nye. Every scientist can recite their scripture: A scientific theory can never be proven—only disproven. No matter how many facts have supported a theory up till now, a single new fact could always come along and render it obsolete.

So why haven't scientists flocked to Ahmedabad? Surely they want to know if the single new fact of Prahlad Jani is the one that disproves the theory that humans need food and water to live. Surely they want to know if new evidence obliges them to rewrite their textbooks. And why haven't scientists investigated the other people from India, and elsewhere in the world, who have also claimed Jani's capacities?

A few doctors from America and Europe did express interest in further investigation of Jani, who has said he would welcome it, but I can find no evidence that any more studies have been done. Jani's extraordinary claims—and the tantalizing results of two official studies—have been neither substantiated nor discredited. They've just been forgotten.

The story *was* reported by mainstream American news agencies, as well as news organizations in other countries. It just didn't make much of an impression. NBC's idea of follow-up was to interview Dr. Michael VanRooyen, director of the Harvard Humanitarian Initiative. VanRooyen knew nothing about the study, but he did believe he knew how to characterize the results: impossible. He added that, "You lose about a liter or two of water per day just by breathing… That water loss results in thicker blood and a drop in blood pressure. You go from being a grape to a raisin." If you didn't have a heart attack first, VanRooyen told the reporter, you'd die of kidney failure. Confronted with the same evidence of potentially earth-shattering importance, ABC opted to interview Keri Gans, a spokeswoman for the American Dietetic Association in New York City. Gans also had no familiarity with the Indian study, but she offered that "you need food to function," and that Jani was "setting himself up for nutritional deficiencies." One can only hope that the words of these two experts somehow reached Jani.

I couldn't help that last sentence. But it's unfair. The news agencies were just ticking boxes. Yes, they interviewed experts. Just not experts about the study. What, one wonders, did anyone expect these "experts" to say? Perhaps, "That's so interesting. It looks like the foundation of everything I've been taught about biology, everything I base my livelihood on, and everything I've experienced, turns out to be wrong. I'd love to hear more, but first let me shut down my organization."

The journalists couldn't call Science for a comment. Like all abstractions, it has no phone number. Like all abstractions, it doesn't exist except in our imagination. The journalists could only call something that does exist—human beings.

Were there such a thing as Science, you couldn't keep it away from Prahlad Jani until it had revealed which one was flawed: the Ahmedabad studies or the foundational laws of biology. That's what this mythical creature Science does—investigate interesting phenomena. It doesn't care about grant money, careers, plane fare, status, awards, speaking fees, social acceptance, or its sense of identity. Unlike the jobs that human beings have, the job of this spirit called Science is simple: give us a clear, unbiased picture of reality. To do this job most effectively, it stands to reason Science should take the greatest interest in what is most fundamental to that picture of reality.

The problem is that human beings almost always do the opposite.

Castle Walls

We don't mind tweaking our picture of reality a little—adding some paint here, tightening up a screw there. We don't mind, in other words, changing the odd minor belief. We call that learning. If you think a tomato is a vegetable, and someone tells you that since it has seeds it's technically a fruit, you're likely to accept the new information. You can, one hopes, get on with your life pretty much as you've been living it. But something paradoxical happens when it comes to matters closer to our hearts and bank accounts. The more important our beliefs, the less important are evidence and logic.

Most of us have encountered someone—whether in a marriage or just on TV—whose views are so stupid it makes you want to strangle them. Our frustration comes from watching them perform a kind of magic act in which we are powerless to intrude. With a wave of their mind, they can make serious challenges disappear.

With another wave, they can conjure elaborate notions from the smallest specks of evidence. They can ignore your facts or statistics and repeat their own ad nauseum. They can dance around a question you're certain would expose how crazy they are. They can refuse to read an essay you're sure would change their mind.

It's as if they live in a castle of belief.

We think our rational arguments should be able to smash through their walls like wrecking balls. Instead, our arguments bounce off those walls like paper airplanes.

Or we imagine we can coax our opponents outside their castle to have a look at more of the world. If you're not an evangelical Christian—or a feminist, or a conservative, or an optimist—it's easy to see how much is outside the castle walls of someone who is. If only they looked at this or that, they would change their minds. But how many arguments about weighty matters are dotted by phrases like, "Hm, I hadn't heard that statistic," "That's an interesting point," "I'll have to look into that," "I could be wrong there." On a list of favorite human activities, contemplating challenges to our fundamental beliefs would probably rank just below stabbing our thighs with a pencil.

Our castle walls are thick. They have to be. They don't protect merely the odd opinion or stray judgment call. They protect a whole nervous system of opinions and judgments that constitutes what we feel to be *us*—our daily activities, our jobs, our friends, how we find some measure of solace and sense.

My wall protects my life. It may not be a great life, but it is *my* life—the life I'm used to. Inside my castle, I know where the kitchen is. Even if it's only stocked with crumbs.

Which brings us back to the man who may not need any kitchen. Prahlad Jani might have been "like a bomb" to Doctor Shah and his colleagues. But the bomb blast in Ahmedabad, India arrived at the castle of Dr. Michael VanRooyen in Cambridge, Massachusetts, in a different form—as a phone call from a reporter no one's heard of, about some studies no one's heard of, by doctors no one's heard of, in a non-Western hospital no one's heard of. What's more, if the studies are true, it would challenge the foundations of VanRooyen's income, status, expertise, and the organization he runs. Dr. Shah's bomb has become Dr. VanRooyen's paper airplane.

It taps his castle wall with barely a sound.

It's easy to imagine a single bomb, like the phenomenon of Prahlad Jani, becoming a single paper airplane that pecks the walls of Western scientists. But if these kinds of bombs were going off all the time, surely the walls of people like VanRooyen and other Western intellectuals would start to wobble. Surely they'd pay more attention.

Isn't Western culture, after all, free from a foundational bias? Isn't that what makes us special? Unlike communist China, a Muslim caliphate, or Medieval Europe, we don't have gatekeepers enforcing a fundamentally distorted vision of the world.

Right?

To casual observation, that seems right. It seems we in the West can find information about anything. Nothing is off limits. Every interest, hobby, fetish, point-of-view, and spiritual belief has its websites, books, magazines, and followers. People like, believe, and spout… everything. In fact, that's just the problem—too much information. How to make sense of it all? And that's exactly where many of us look to Science. Science is our sober filter, separating the valid from the vapid. To avoid being gullible, smart people tend to look to Science for guidance.

Science, after all, does the research.

How to Belong

Well, not quite. Science can't do any research. Science doesn't have a lab. Or even a pencil or a hand to hold it. It bears repeating because it has fundamental consequences for what many of us believe about reality: Science doesn't exist. It's human beings who do the research.

If Science did research, that research would be flawless. Since human beings do it, "the majority of papers that get published, even in serious journals, are pretty sloppy." This at any rate is the conclusion of Stanford's John Ioannidis, a pioneer in the study of scientific research itself. Ioannidis wasn't kidding when he titled his 2005 article, "Why Most Published Research Findings are False." "For most study designs and settings, it is more likely for a research claim to be false than true," he writes. "Moreover, for many current scientific fields, claimed research findings may often simply be accurate measures of the prevailing bias."

How can this be?

In a word, incentives.

Who, in an official capacity, had an incentive to find out more about Prahlad Jani? Not only would a serious investigation take time and money, it would also require looking foolish for showing an interest. And the payoff for such a hypothetical investigation? Either Jani is a hoax and you've wasted resources and invited further ridicule, or Jani is for real and you've discovered something that's too radical to incorporate into existing institutions and beliefs.

The infinitely more attractive option for almost all scientists is to ignore Prahlad Jani.

The incentive of our fictional superhero, Science, is pure and simple: Find out about reality. Science doesn't care about its career or whether a study it's been toiling over for years turns out to be important or inconsequential. Scientists, however, do care. And if Ioannidis is right that most research findings are false, they care a lot. Enough to systematically ignore the principles of good Science. While most scientists may be good people who want their studies to be accurate, most also want their hypotheses to be right, their results to be splashy, their papers to be published, their brilliance to be praised, and their careers to be advanced. The incentive for staying absolutely true to the spirit of Science is much less compelling—a warm, fuzzy feeling that you did the right cold, logical thing.

Some scientists care so much about all-too-human incentives that they commit fraud. Daniele Fanelli, who worked with Ioannidis, analyzed the results of eighteen separate anonymous surveys and concluded that one out of fifty scientists admit to at least one case of fabrication, falsification, or other "cooking" of data. The actual number must be substantially higher if another of Fanelli's findings is right: More than one in ten scientists report seeing this behavior in their peers. We'll never know the actual frequency of scientific fraud. But we can probably agree that it's higher than scientists either admit or discover.

OK, so scientists are humans. They warm up a little data here, ignore the odd miracle report there. They have social lives, careers, and money to worry about, just like the next guy. But surely none of this adds up to a conspiracy to keep evidence of a spiritual world out of official Western awareness. Don't Western scientists, after all, represent something special in human history—the end of all conspiracies against the truth? Unlike, say, evangelical ministers, scientists have no baked-in bias, no systematic leaning towards certain kinds of evidence and away from others. The scattered bricks of a little subjective bias among scientists don't add up to a wall designed to keep huge spiritual vistas from our view.

Do they?

Every group has some combination of rules, routines, and expectations—even if they are all unspoken. Without this collective culture, you don't have a group—just an assortment of individuals who happen to bump into each other every once in a while. Without a collective culture, no one consistently meets up; and if they happen to, they don't talk about the same things. Nothing gets done. No activities get planned, no buildings get built, no letters after your name get issued. In the hugeness of reality, a group's culture focuses it on certain possibilities—and therefore away from others. The very rules, routines, and expectations that make a group possible also wall that group off from parts of a wider reality.

Groups are also self-reinforcing. To be in the community of Western scientists is to train in its institutions for years. Who chooses to do this? The kind of person who is attracted to the culture and interests of these institutions. What happens in these institutions? Their culture and interests are further reinforced and rewarded. True believers go in; extra-true believers come out.

Scientists further reinforce their surrounding walls the way all groups do—by giving their biggest rewards to their truest believers. The rewards include positions of power and influence, along with the money and admiration that come with those positions. These truest believers—whom we could also call those most indoctrinated—therefore have the greatest influence on the group's perpetuation and become the members most visible to the public. They are also the very people with the biggest incentives to defend the castle. After all, they're getting the best food in its kitchen. Groups are perfect breeding grounds for the human tendency to double-down on our castle walls.

Hippies don't join the Navy. Neither do those inclined to believe in a spiritual world—or who have had experiences in that world—generally become scientists. The rules, expectations, and routines of scientists may be spoken or unspoken. But to belong to their group is to gaze in certain directions and to be driven by certain incentives.

And not by others.

Stranger than Fiction

What incentives, I wonder, did Michael Crichton have for writing a book in 1988 that you've probably never heard of. He didn't need money or fame or any more degrees. He had already graduated *summa cum laude* from Harvard and earned an MD at Harvard Medical School. But the unfeeling culture of med school put him off, and he'd decided not to practice medicine. Instead, he had become the best-selling author of *The Andromeda Strain*, *The Great Train Robbery*, and *Congo*, all of which had been made into hit movies, one of which he had directed. By 1988 Crichton's career as a novelist and Hollywood player was in full swing and it would only get better from there.

Yet in that year, Crichton took the time to write *Travels*, a work of non-fiction that recounts his departure from the world of medicine and his exploration of the greater world. Among the experiences he describes are his encounters with what many scientists would call nonsense. He visits, for example, several psychics while in London to shoot a film, using a fake name and doing his best to give them as little as possible to go on. Some of the psychics fail to impress him. He is unable to explain the accuracy of others.

Unfettered by the rules, routines, and expectations that usually accompany a string of letters after your name, Crichton explored still other disreputable phenomena. In 1985, he attended a spoon-bending party, hosted by an aerospace engineer named Jack Houck, who told guests to bring silverware from home. The guests were instructed to work themselves into an excited state and shout, "Bend! Bend!" at a spoon of their choice, and then relax and lightly rub said cutlery. After seeing others succeed and becoming frustrated that he wasn't, Crichton gave up, idly stroking his utensil while his attention wandered. Soon after that, one of his companions pointed out that his spoon was bending. He went on to easily bend several spoons and forks before becoming more interested in seeing what kinds of snacks they had.

Many intelligent people in the West rightly give scientists the benefit of the doubt. After hearing that researchers sometimes fudge data and often publish "pretty sloppy" papers, we shouldn't assume the next scientist we encounter is a fraud or an idiot. At the very least, reasonable people judge each scientist's veracity on a case-by-case basis. This attitude towards scientists—which is itself scientific—is easy to maintain in our culture.

But when it comes to the paranormal, many intelligent people aren't as generous—or as true to the ideals of Science. Having heard that debunkers like James Randi have exposed some fake spoon-benders, our culture makes it easy to assume that spoon-bending is therefore always an illusion and that anyone who believes it's possible must be either a fraud or an idiot.

Crichton wrote in *Travels*, "I had bent a spoon, and I *knew* it wasn't a trick." Was Michael Crichton—Harvard M.D., successful novelist, Hollywood director—a fraud or an idiot?

Or was he just a neutral observer?

Crichton didn't need *Travels* to make money, gain notoriety, earn a degree, look impressive, or gain entrée into any group. Unlike Randi, whose identity is tied to debunking, Crichton didn't mount a crusade for spoon-bending. It was just an experience he had. He concludes that it seemed to require a "focused inattention." You had to first try hard and then forget about it. Achieving this focused inattention took learning, but once learned, it was easy. Even boring. Crichton in fact came to feel this way in general about the various paranormal phenomena he experienced. At first they seem amazing, but pretty quickly become mundane, like doing the laundry or riding a bike. Over the course of his experiences, Crichton came to believe there is nothing *para* about paranormal abilities: "We've just forgotten we can do them."

And as a culture, we've forgotten Crichton's book.

Or, more accurately, we barely paid attention to it. Like Prahlad Jani, or the pervasive sloppiness of scientific papers, Crichton's experiences don't exist in most people's reality. *Travels* barely caused a blip on our cultural radar screen. On his 8700-word Wikipedia page, for example, each of Crichton's novels gets a paragraph or two, with plot descriptions and background information. *Travels* gets ten words: "A book of autobiographical writings, *Travels* was published in 1988." We are happy to remember Crichton the thriller fiction writer. But what was arguably his most amazing book bounced off the culture like a paper airplane bounces off a castle wall.

How many of these airplanes are out there?

Psychiatrist Elisabeth Kübler-Ross had one. But she chose not to even throw it. Dr. Kübler-Ross rose into public awareness in 1969 with her groundbreaking book, *On Death and Dying*, which outlined the five stages of grief and ushered in a new humanity in our treatment of the terminally ill. Over her career, she received nineteen honorary degrees and was inducted into the National Women's Hall of Fame in 2007. What hardly anyone knows is that during the time that inspired her classic book, Kübler-Ross—and the hospital chaplain assigned to accompany her on her visits to the dying—heard stories over and over of encounters with spirits, as well as near-death and out-of-body experiences. A little girl gave a description of a man who came to visit her which matched a dead uncle she'd never seen. A woman accurately described the doodles on a nurse's pad which she'd seen from above the nurse as she floated outside her body. The stories were so persistent, similar, and compelling that, to write an authentic book, Kübler-Ross felt she had to dedicate the final chapter to them.

And so she did. What, after all, could be a bigger bomb than strong evidence for life after death? When it came time for the final edit, though, both Kübler-Ross and the chaplain realized that if they kept that last chapter, the credibility of the rest of the book would plummet. She had a choice: be taken seriously in her field or tell the entire truth. The book ended up making a splash. The last chapter made no appearance. Both Crichton and Kübler-Ross had M.D.s after their names. But only Kübler-Ross's success depended on the approval of a wider group of M.D.s.

Because Kübler-Ross wanted to be taken seriously by the establishment, she could only afford to be just so groundbreaking in her book. As far as nearly everyone on the planet is concerned, the stories she found so convincing in her hospital rounds don't exist. Her 1969 classic *On Death and Dying*, published by the prestigious Scribner house, is "one of the most famous psychological studies of the late twentieth century." Her 1991 book *On Life After Death*, published by the lesser known Celestial Arts of Berkeley, is effectively invisible. Her Wikipedia profile will not enlighten you about her compelling spiritual experiences with the dying. Instead it describes how she was duped later in life by a scam artist masquerading as a spirit-channeler. Once again, our cultural waters encourage us to file anyone interested in the spirit world under the category "fruitcake," and get on with our lives.

Speaking in Public

The Spanish writer and philosopher Miguel de Unamuno wrote that, "the greatest height of heroism to which an individual... can attain is to know how to face ridicule." This makes sense given that public speaking is usually just *above* death on the average person's list of things they fear the most, and that soldiers regularly choose death over appearing weak to their comrades. If Unamuno is right, then in today's Western culture, talking about paranormal experiences you've had—whether voices, visions, visitations, out-of-body experiences, or ESP—is an act of heroism.

It wasn't always that way. In her book, *Joan of Arc: A History*, Helen Castor writes,

> There seems little purpose... in attempting to diagnose in [Joan] a physical or psychological disorder that might, to us, explain her voices, if the terms of reference we use are completely alien to the landscape of belief in which she lived. Joan and the people around her knew that it was entirely possible for other-worldly beings to communicate with men and women of sound mind.

The oxygen in the cultural air around Joan ignited the fuel of her visions. The combination propelled her on a three-hundred-mile journey from her village through enemy territory to the royal court, where she continued burning brightly enough to convince a king to place her at the head of an army. Her subsequent victories turned the tide for France against the occupying English in the Hundred Years War, as Joan transformed "a dry dynastic squabble... into a passionately popular war of national liberation."

Today the sparks of Joan's visions would be denied that cultural oxygen. Instead, they'd almost certainly be smothered if not by ridicule, then by indifference, disbelief, or medication. They wouldn't of course even be called sparks; they'd be herded into the ghetto called hallucinations. Rather than bending the ears of presidents and changing the course of history, Joan would more likely be found behind a register at Wendy's, zonked out on possibly legal drugs; or living in a cabin, quietly painting pictures of fantastic beings.

Or she may be living next door to you. In his book, *Hallucinations,* neurologist Oliver Sacks writes that while hallucinations are today "often considered to portend madness or something dire happening in the brain, the vast majority… have no such dark implications." Instead, Sacks points out, hearing non-physical voices, as well as seeing non-physical things, is not uncommon among perfectly sane people. Indeed, his book is devoted to such phenomena, which go massively under-reported. Socrates, Freud, Jung, Dickens, Dostoyevsky, Schumann, Churchill, William Blake, Philip K. Dick, and Anthony Hopkins have all been visited and had the courage to testify.

One doesn't usually lead with such topics at cocktail parties. But show an openness to other-worldly phenomena with people around you, and it's amazing how many will admit to experiencing one or two of them—whether a premonitory dream, a voice, or a visit from a ghost. I've spoken with several people who've left their bodies, heard guiding voices, or seen ghostly figures. One acquaintance told me she left her body regularly as a child and thought it the most natural thing in the world. She soon learned to stop talking about it—and then to stop doing it. A family friend was led to safety out of and away from the World Trade Center on 9/11 by a voice. She did not mention that part of the story to the journalists who interviewed her.

Would you?

Chronicling the Wondrous

Expand our perspective on the supernatural across more peoples and times, and a paradox emerges. In the words of Jeffrey Kripal, a Professor of Philosophy and Religious Thought at Rice University, "If we collect enough seemingly anecdotal or anomalous experiences from different times and places… we can quickly see that these reports are neither anecdotal nor anomalous. We can see that they are actually common occurrences in the species."

Not only common but hugely consequential for the culture. All the West's major religions are founded around mystical visions and miraculous events—Moses before the burning bush, Jesus healing the sick and raising the dead, Mohammad's visitations from the angel Gabriel. The apostle Paul's relentless preaching and the emperor Constantine's legalization of the faith were arguably the two greatest factors in the success of Christianity. Both men were converted when they experienced dramatic visions. The modern spiritual teacher Eckhart Tolle describes a similar spiritual epiphany during which he heard a voice say, "Resist nothing."

Jesus and Mohammad—and perhaps Paul, Constantine, and Tolle as well—sparked what University of Pennsylvania anthropologist Anthony Wallace called "revitalization movements." In a 1956 study, Wallace defined such a movement as "a deliberate, organized, conscious effort by members of a society to construct a more satisfying culture." Wallace analyzed several hundred such movements from five continents, ranging from the new religion of the Seneca prophet Handsome Lake in North America to the Sudanese Mahdi in Africa, from the Taiping Rebellion in China to a series of *terre sans mal* movements among forest tribes of South America. Wallace wrote, "With a few exceptions, every religious revitalization movement with which I am acquainted has been originally conceived in one or several hallucinatory visions by a single individual." Gandhi, who led India to independence, heard a guiding voice that was "as unmistakable as some human voice definitely speaking to me." The skeptic, said Gandhi, "is free to say that it was all self-delusion or hallucination... But I can say this, that not the unanimous verdict of the whole world against me could shake me from the belief that what I heard was the true Voice of God." I've yet to see that quote in a history textbook.

Voices, visions, and visitations have by no means been confined to singular cultural heroes. Aside from the wondrous phenomena said to surround its founding figure, the Christian tradition has been rife with them ever since—not just as undocumented myths, but often attested to by well-respected eyewitnesses. Many of these accounts are made even more credible by the fact that they were a source of embarrassment to the Church—not because its authorities doubted the reality of other-worldly visitors, but because they often judged them more ghoulish than godly. The ecstatic visions of the seventeenth-century Franciscan Joseph of Copertino got him booted from the first order of friars he joined. He managed to gain acceptance into a second order, where his visions continued, now with the addition of involuntary levitations, often during mass. This was considered highly disruptive. Eventually he was sequestered and received a visit from the Inquisition. Copertino's levitations are extensively documented in contemporary letters, diaries, official documents, paintings, inscriptions on relics and monuments, and testified to under oath by over a hundred and fifty eyewitnesses.

Copertino's story is just one example among hundreds of what we now call supernatural phenomena that were interpreted according to the Christian context of their times. The most well-known of such phenomena is the appearance of the stigmata—the wounds of Christ—on the hands and feet of several hundred particularly fervent Christian mystics. St. Francis, whom some of have called Christ's closest imitator—lover of nature, peace, and poverty—was among the earliest to receive these wounds, during a vision of a six-winged seraph on a cross.

The so-called anomalous sprouts up in every religious tradition. In India, the miraculous doings of holy men, including healings and the Christ-like multiplication of food, are part of the religious landscape, attested to for centuries. Prahlad Jani, our man who claims to have opted out of the whole bodily function thing, is just one of many. Countless eyewitnesses, for example, tell stories of the healing, clairvoyant, and other miraculous powers of Bhagawan Nityananda of Ganeshpuri, who died in 1961 after a lifetime marked by the simplest living, providing for the poor, and no interest whatsoever in notoriety or money. Amazing and strange figures doing things we Westerners would dismiss off-hand also populate the history of mystical Islam. Shaman-figures were central to many tribal societies. Part doctor, part priest, part showman, their role was to navigate other worlds for the benefit of both individuals and the tribe as a whole.

But for many tribal cultures, communion with a spirit world wasn't left only to specialists. Boys being initiated into men went alone into the wilds to wait for the vision that would help them know who they were. Animistic and pagan peoples felt their world as alive with spirits and gods and often literally saw these beings, just as the poet William Blake saw angels and Carl Jung conversed with a spirit guide. Oliver Sacks points out that the word *hallucination* wasn't used for such phenomena until around 1830. Before that, they were called apparitions. Sacks writes that "many cultures regard hallucination… as a special, privileged state of consciousness—one that is actively sought through spiritual practices, meditation, drugs, or solitude."

Invisible Walls

Mainstream scientists often tout an open-mindedness before baffling facts as a requirement in their field—or as one of its defining characteristics. This openness is the very thing that has led to new scientific insights, or even revolutions. Einstein's bold explanation for the baffling behavior of light in the early twentieth century led to the quantum revolution and the modern digital age.

But some kinds of baffling phenomena meet a barrier in the scientific community. Sociologist James McClenon writes that these "scientific boundaries are not created by philosophical argument." Instead, they are practical: "Scientific institutions do not have sufficient time and money to investigate extremely far-fetched theories."

These practical boundaries are, in turn, based on temperament. Taking 'fringe' ideas seriously is not a typical trait in the psychological profile of a scientist. Professor emeritus of Natural Science Michael Swords puts it more bluntly: "The majority of the scientific community is a very non-risk-taking group of people that live in a rather small reality and are in fact scared of things which seem to be outside that reality." Thomas Kuhn, perhaps the most influential modern philosopher of science, has written that mainstream science "often suppresses fundamental novelties because they are… subversive of its basic commitments."

Scientific institutions and their funding are built on those basic commitments. There are zero economic or social incentives to investigate what everyone's already decided is nuts. In this environment, taking the paranormal seriously would require much effort while also likely hindering your career. The choice not to take it seriously, then, is a no-brainer.

Convenience is a perfectly good reason to do or not do something. But it has nothing to do with finding out what reality is like. As another prominent philosopher of science has noted, "A little brainwashing will go a long way" in making science seem like a purely objective consideration of the evidence. Without realizing it, many scientists have brainwashed themselves. They've performed a collective act of magic, transforming a convenient choice into a grand philosophical truth: 'The reason we don't investigate paranormal phenomena is not because that investigation would be confusing, time-consuming, expensive, and harmful to our careers. No. The reason we don't investigate paranormal phenomena is because they aren't real.'

Scientists who persist in public display of an open mind to the paranormal face not only the ridicule of peers, but often their outright malice. As part of his PhD dissertation in sociology at the University of Maryland, James McClenon mailed a questionnaire about ESP to elite members of the Association of the Advancement of Science. Five or six of them were so vexed that they wrote letters urging McClenon be kicked out of graduate school. Others returned the questionnaire with agitated notes in the margin, one of which read, "I feel like you're trying to hurt us." McClenon said it was depressing for a fledgling sociologist, but that he was "at the same time a bit thrilled. It seemed like I was putting my finger on some kind of strange nerve."

Other researchers of the paranormal in the seventies and early eighties touched the same strange nerve. Their work sparked such a fevered debate with skeptics that some sociologists became interested not in who was right, but in the argument itself. They were surprised to find that parapsychology researchers often bent over backwards to produce papers that were more scientifically rigorous than most mainstream papers. Sociologists were also surprised by the shrillness and ideological fanaticism of many of the skeptics.

Astronomy professor J. Allen Hynek was such a skeptic when the U.S. Air Force asked him to help debunk a growing number of UFO reports in the sixties. He accepted, "almost in a sense of sport," assuming it would be an opportunity to "educate the public about how the scientific method works," and "clear away non-science." Instead, he came to appreciate almost the opposite. Over twenty years of investigating UFO reports, Hynek found "beyond a reasonable doubt that they are not all misperceptions or hoaxes."

Hynek also gained some perspective on the prevailing attitude among his academic colleagues, writing that their "emotionally loaded, highly exaggerated reaction… to any mention of UFOs might be of considerable interest to psychologists."

It's as if the paranormal is to scientists what sex is to puritans. Obscene. And yet, ubiquitous.

The CIA can afford to be more openminded towards the paranormal, at least if they can find a use for it. And apparently they have. Project Stargate, declassified in 2000, officially concluded that remote viewing "works with remarkable precision," and that "remote viewers can be used as collectors in conjunction with other intelligence sources throughout the DoD intelligence community." Their findings also echoed Crichton's hunch that what we think of as weird abilities are just like any other skill that can lie dormant or flourish with practice. According to the CIA, remote viewing is "a talent which is inherent to every human to some degree," and which "through proper training can be developed to a person's potential." It's just that this particular skill is "largely ignored in today's societal setting." It's a funny world when the CIA and Lewis Carroll are on the same page. "One can't believe impossible things," says Carroll's Alice to the Queen. "I daresay you haven't had much practice," says the Queen back.

In the 1990s, the CIA asked statistics professor Jessica Utts to assess the evidence for psychic functioning. They didn't pick Utts at random. She is the author of mainstream textbooks such as *Seeing Through Statistics,* a guide to "the key concepts that educated citizens need to know about statistics," and in 2016 was elected the 111th president of The American Statistical Association, "the world's largest community of statisticians." In her CIA-funded 1996 paper, "An Assessment of the Evidence for Psychic Functioning," Utts writes, "Using the standards applied to any other area of science, it is concluded that psychic functioning has been well established. The statistical results of the studies examined are far beyond what is expected by chance. Arguments that these results could be due to methodological flaws in the experiments are soundly refuted."

Naked Truth

If you're like me, it comes as a minor shock that a president of America's foremost group of statisticians and a mainstream textbook author has written the clear statement, "Psychic functioning has been well-established." Why haven't we heard this? Why isn't there a chapter on psychic ability in our Psychology 101 textbooks? The shock arises because most of us have innocently believed—as sociologist James McClenon once did—that a fictional hero called Science really rules our academic institutions. In our imagination, this hero flies around investigating any and all phenomena and then offers his reports through unbiased institutions whose only concern is the truth.

But this innocence doesn't reckon with the castle walls that all groups of people in the real world build around themselves. You haven't heard professor Utts's unqualified trumpet blast confirming psychic functioning because—even though it came from a fellow academic—it still didn't shake the invisible wall surrounding the official beliefs of scientists. It became a paper airplane that lightly tapped the same wall tapped by the Indian doctors' research on Prahlad Jani, Michael Crichton's account of bending spoons, Kübler-Ross's experience with compelling evidence for a spirit world, Professor Hynek's UFO findings, or the CIA's conclusions about remote viewing. It's the collective wall of a unique group of human beings we call scientists who have a unique mix of interests. Only one of these interests is to discover the nature of ultimate reality.

Our weightiest arguments are almost always decided before they start—by the premises we accept. And before that, by the incentives that drive those premises. The capacity of properly incentivized groups to ignore the obvious is astonishing. It's the principle behind the oft-cited story of the naked emperor. Whether you're the Spanish Inquisition or the Psychology Department at Yale, when you begin an investigation married to certain assumptions, then certain conclusions are foregone. And certain pieces of evidence—like an emperor's rosy ass cheeks—are simply ignored.

Conventional medicine has been staring at a pair of ass cheeks for centuries. In keeping with the official version of Western science, Western medicine's image of the body is fundamentally mechanical.

We are cars; doctors mechanics. And faith-healers are, of course, crackpots. This despite the fact that faith-healing has happened all over the globe and throughout human history. In the fluorescent-lit halls of our Western institutions, we call it the placebo effect. Aside from thousands of cases of spontaneous remission from all manner of illnesses that doctors deemed irreversible, studies have over and over revealed the power of belief on our bodies. People get relief from vomiting when told a substance will help, even when that substance is actually ipecac, which is normally used to *induce* vomiting; fake knee surgery is found to be every bit as effective as actual surgery; a Harvard study supports the hypothesis that "exercise affects health in part or in whole via the placebo effect." Whenever possible, researchers acknowledge the reality of the placebo effect by designing studies that are double-blind, meaning they keep both experimenters and subjects unaware of who is getting the actual treatment so that no one's beliefs can interfere with the results.

In the words of one doctor, Lissa Rankin, "The medical establishment has been proving for over fifty years that the mind can heal the body" via the placebo effect. But instead of cause for celebration, Rankin points out, it is for Western medicine "an inconvenient truth." It complicates research whose aim is not to explore the capacities of human beings but to develop drugs and procedures that can be sold to those human beings. There are few cultural institutions where the paramount incentive is to look within.

Serpents & Doves

Science may be a purely fictional hero. But it has been alive enough in our flesh-and-blood scientists to have guided the creation of wonders, from electricity to air-conditioning, iPhones, and super-powered tomatoes. And like all ideals, its lack of physical existence is its very strength. The spirit of Science, however diluted, does not reside exclusively in a group of indoctrinated professionals. If it did, a PhD-less nobody with a nine-to-five job would not have been allowed to suggest that $E=mc^2$, and thereby give birth to the digital age and a radical new vision of reality. The spirit of Science—that ideal openness to all phenomena—may in fact find its purest form outside any official group. Free from the need to seek consensus, compromise, or approval, the single soul may be the most trenchant seeker of truth—whether a truth for that soul only, for a community, or for the world.

Groups serve valuable purposes and are a central part of being human. But we can be shrewd when we weigh their pronouncements. Paradoxically, it is just this shrewdness that can allow us to maintain our innocence before the world—to stand by our own experience. In the famous fable, it's a child who blurts the truth about the emperor's naked ass. And in the New Testament, it's that faith-healer Jesus who advises us to "become as little children" if we want to enter the kingdom of heaven, which according to Eckhart Tolle is just to see this world clearly as a window on eternity. But Jesus advises shrewdness as well. When he sends his own renegade group of disciples forth, he counsels them to be "wise as serpents and innocent as doves." A serpent shrewdly sniffs out the hidden assumptions, invested authorities, and knee-jerk ridicule that come with institutions. Doves—Michael Crichton, Elisabeth Kübler-Ross, Joan of Arc, Gandhi, Einstein, you, and me—are free to fly where we will.

II. Who Should We Ask About God?

Do Scientists Know What Reality Is?

"The world and I are within one another."

—Maurice Merleau-Ponty

At the beginning of his book, *Enlightenment Now*, Steven Pinker writes of a young woman who asks him a question after a talk he has just given about "the common-place among scientists that mental life consists of patterns of activity in the tissues of the brain." Pinker is a cognitive psychologist and linguist, and his book is a celebration of Science—of everything those "patterns of activity in the tissues of the brain" have done for us. The young woman's question was "Why should I live?"

If Pinker were a carpenter who had just given a talk about the accomplishments of his trade—displaying photographs of ornate desks and elegant chairs—the young woman would not have asked him this. We don't believe carpenters—except for the one—are especially qualified to answer our deepest questions about life. To the young woman in the audience though, Pinker is.

New Priests

The young woman was, essentially, looking for God. And she thought Pinker might be an expert.

In the past we went to our local high priest, or the equivalent, to find God—to find out what was important, what was real. Perhaps the priest announced that a blemish on a sacrificial bull would displease the gods and cause the crops to fail. The bull's blemish was taken as important, as real. So were the gods and their disapproval of it. These realities were final—there was no seeing through or behind them, no appealing to something more real.

We no longer believe we need to sacrifice a bull to keep our crops from failing, but we may believe we need to sacrifice fatty foods to keep our hearts from failing. Today, many of us look to Science for the ultimate truth—the backstop of all backstops. The young woman asked Pinker her question because for her and many other intelligent people, scientists are the modern high priests.

Their pronouncements are everywhere. We see them in the latest headline. "New Study Shows…" fill in the blank: "Red Wine Lowers Blood Pressure," "Red Wine Raises Blood Pressure," "Is Your Milk Killing You?" and on and on. And on. On a grander scale, we read their pronouncements in books like Pinker's, or any number of other popular books by astrophysicists or evolutionary biologists who seek to enlighten the public about the truths of the universe.

Like many of these books, *Enlightenment Now* is fascinating and helpful. (Pinker's section on our insistence that the world is getting worse, despite overwhelming evidence that it's getting better, should be required reading.) And like many of these books, Pinker's encourages the ordainment of scientists in the new priesthood.

Some authors encourage this ordainment more strongly than others. Pinker isn't out to demolish spirituality. Then again, that's only because he believes it's already a heap of rubble. He takes it as a given that the laws of Science rule the universe. Pinker's book sounds the same note as those of many of his fellow scientists. While claiming an essential modesty for their field—'a scientific theory is always vulnerable to being disproven, there is so much more to know about this or that, we must always keep an open mind to new evidence'—they nonetheless appear to believe Science is mighty enough to weigh in on the biggest questions.

Its answers are not encouraging. We are no longer beings made in the image of God. We are instead the result of eons of random mutations, some of which happen to be helpful in the ruthless competition of natural selection. There are no angels above. Rather, the universe is an endless void filled with stars, planets, dust, and movies about super-heroes. There are no more good endings. Spoiler alert:

The laws of physics guarantee that disorder must always increase until everything decays into a perfectly uniform mess. And when you die? There is no after-life. Only one very long nap.

So says Science. Should we believe it?

We've seen what Science can do for us. We peck at and peer into what Science has done for us every few minutes. We ride in it, live in it, wear it, and eat it.

We've also seen what traditional religion cannot do for us. It cannot give us the conveniences and certainties that Science can. It cannot give us rational explanations for why things are as they are. A thinking person might accept an irrational account of the universe—a concession to mystery—if there were only one such account on offer. But there are by some estimates 35,000 Christian denominations alone, never mind the varieties of Islam, Hinduism, Buddhism, or Judaism. For anyone not born into a tradition, choosing from among these truths must resemble choosing a novel from the shelves of a bookstore.

Can Science somehow be our new religion? Was the young woman wise to ask her question to Pinker?

Thomas Edison said, "I can never find the thing that does the job the best until I find the ones that don't." The job the young woman is asking Science to do is a big one. If Science is qualified to do it, that would be good to know. If it is not, that would also be helpful. We would know another place in the bookstore not to look.

Reality Room

Imagine looking, not for a book, but for a mouse in a room. If a group of self-proclaimed experts on the contents of the room were to announce, "There is no mouse in this room," we could take their word for it. But if we cared deeply whether there was a mouse in the room, we'd be more insistent. One of the first things we'd ask is whether the experts had looked everywhere in the room. Is there an area under the bed they hadn't seen? An extra nook around a corner they hadn't noticed? The experts must know what the room is, before they can say there's no mouse in it.

The same requirement applies to a scientist who announces that God is not real. The biologist and prominent atheist Richard Dawkins, for example, must know what this room called "reality" is before he can announce that God is not in it.

Has Dawkins or Pinker mapped this room? Has anyone?

What is reality?

* * *

Reality is first and foremost a word. One of the many we're steeped in every day. We communicate—or think we do—using words with our family, friends, and co-workers. We understand—or think we do—through reading words about politics, social issues, or psychology.

Our intellectual culture is based on words. They make things official, even real. We're impressed when something can be articulated with language. An inarticulate person is taken to be a fool. I've caught myself falling under this spell when I reflexively underestimate the intelligence of a foreign visitor simply because their English is rudimentary.

But eloquence can cast another kind of spell. The smooth flow of words can misdirect. We can be carried along, as on a fast-moving stream, hypnotized by the sparkle of words like *aplomb* and *crepuscular,* until we find ourselves deposited far from the place we wanted to go. The wordsmith Saul Bellow noted that, "A great deal of intelligence can be invested in ignorance when the need for illusion is deep."

One of the illusions we are swept along by every day is that we know what the words we're using mean. Or that they have a precise meaning at all.

The more specific and practical a word, the less its meaning is a problem. If I asked you to walk around your house and make a list of all the "yellow" things, the two of us would probably agree about most of what goes on the list. Or, if I asked you to "wash my car," we'd probably agree on what needs to be done. You'll put some soap and water in a bucket, get a hose, and so forth.

But even in the simplest use of words, ambiguity lurks. There's a good chance you and I would disagree about whether a few items in your house qualify as yellow. Is that pillow yellow or orange? Is that mug yellow or tan? And in the simple request to wash my car, there is also wiggle room. Did I mean you to include the tires? Did I expect you to dry it as well? (Answer to both: I did.)

As words get more general, the vagueness increases. "Wash my car," is child's play compared to "I love you." I'm old enough to know that when someone says that, it could mean anything from "Let's get married" to "I feel pretty good today."

The word *reality* is as general as words get. And therefore as vague as words get. And yet, how often intelligent people assume that we can talk about "reality" as if we all know what it is. If asked to pause and consider what we mean by that word, it's tempting to answer that it's obvious what's real—what's real is what's obvious. Reality is this—what I can see and hear and touch right here.

But this definition of reality leaves out the bedroom upstairs, as well as your mother-in-law, if she's not around at the moment. Most of us want our bedrooms included in reality, and a lower but still significant percentage want our absent mothers-in-law included as well. We also want previously visited forests, fields, towns, and countries included. Conventional wisdom holds that reality encompasses not only what we're perceiving now, but anything we've perceived in the past and believe we could perceive again.

Are we done clarifying a definition of reality? Only if we arbitrarily say we are. We could legitimately ask more questions. Is the town you grew up in real? It's hard to say yes or no. The town may be different now—the corner store has disappeared, a new baseball field went in. The same logic could apply to a sports team. A Dallas Cowboys fan casually speaks of his team as a real thing, though it may not consist of any of the same players, coaches, or owners that it did when he adopted it. As the Cowboys cycle through personnel, so our bodies cycle through atoms. Is your body real? Which one? Maybe we can't say a town, team, or body is technically real. Maybe only the things that make them up are. But those things change too. Those things are made of more things.

Do these questions have answers? Or do they only lead to more questions? The corner store that disappeared, for instance. Assuming it was one real thing—and not the many things it was made of—was it real once, but real no more? Did it enjoy only temporary reality status? What of people that have passed away? Did their reality visas expire?

The jungle we've entered is disorienting enough if we consider only our experience. But most of us don't need to have experienced something to call it real. We're willing to take the word of others. We believe Calcutta is real—however vaguely defined—even if we've never been there. We believe kangaroos are real even if we've never seen one in person. Bigfoot haunts the borderlands of reality. Hundreds of eyewitness accounts date back to colonial times, some of the modern ones bolstered by videos and photos. But only some believe—about twenty percent of Americans, according to a 2014 survey. For most, it seems, grainy images and the testimony of strangers aren't enough.

For some reason, the same kind of evidence is more convincing when it comes to the reality of aliens visiting Earth. About forty percent of Americans are inclined to believe this has happened. The reality of ghosts gets even more votes—about sixty percent of us say yea. Had a question about Jupiter or Alpha Centauri been included in the survey, I assume their reality would receive close to a one hundred percent approval rating. And yet—while at least some people claim firsthand experience of Bigfoot, UFOs, and ghosts—no one has firsthand experience of either of these heavenly bodies.

The same can be said of atoms, which have never been touched nor seen by the naked eye. But the grainy images and testimony of strangers are more compelling when it comes to atoms than when it comes to Bigfoot. It helps that the strangers taking the blurry photos have PhDs and well-funded departments in most universities. It also helps that theories based on the reality of atoms help us accomplish practical things. It's hard to imagine a useful theory based on Bigfoot.

Practicality could explain why Americans are as likely to believe in Bigfoot as in the Big Bang. It's unclear what the advantage is to thinking the entire Universe was once millions of times smaller than a grain of sand and then exploded outwards. Darwin's theory of evolution may suffer from a similar lack of application to our everyday lives. Only about thirty percent of Americans are willing to call it real. Maybe it's more useful to believe we were made in the image of God.

We've wandered deep in the jungle of what we mean by *reality* now. Darwin's theory of evolution isn't a physical thing. Unlike bedrooms, corner stores, mothers-in-law, Bigfoot, or Jupiter, it's impossible to directly experience it. It's made of nothing. Like a ghost. And yet, it's fair to say most people consider at least a few things made of nothing to be real. If natural selection is not your cup of reality, you can probably find something to like in the grab-bag of energy, movement, pressure, the force of gravity, electric fields, freedom, causation, evil, and love. Widespread agreement about which of these invisible things are real, on the other hand, is definitely non-existent.

What's a reasonable person, in search of a definition of reality, to do? If we ask a poet, we're liable to get an answer like Wallace Stevens's, who opined that "Reality is not what it is. It consists of the many realities that it can be made into." Thank you, Wallace. You can sit down now.

Actually, Stevens's answer may not be as crazy as it first sounds. Or perhaps it is just as crazy as it needs to be, given the subject. If reality is a function of permanence, then physical things are often less real than the invisible ideas we each make them into. You and your father have different ideas about your hometown. Both of those ideas may last longer than the physical town. The idea of love has lasted longer than empires.

The poet's answer, though, is too mushy for many reasonable people. It feels improvised. Wallace Stevens may have won the Pulitzer Prize, but it was for writing obscure verse, not for defining reality. For earnest, rational people, like the young woman in Pinker's audience, a poet's opinion is a bauble, nothing to base a life on.

Science, with its systematic textbooks, rigorous equations, and concrete achievements, appears to offer something more dependable. Like many intelligent people, the young woman hoped that scientists like Pinker could offer her an asphalt path through the jungle of reality—a path marked at intervals by those signs that tell us what to notice and, by omission, what to ignore. A path to show her what's really real. The young woman didn't ask Pinker what, according to Science, *reality* is. But her question assumes he knows.

Does he?

Does any scientist?

Mansions of Physics

Google "greatest scientists in history," and you'll notice that an Englishman from the late 1600s tends to top the lists. Isaac Newton was an industrious man. He invented Calculus, improved telescopes, and made groundbreaking discoveries about light. But he's best known for his laws of motion. From planets to pomegranates, he discovered the mathematical logic that guides how things move in the universe. In the Scientific Revolution's shattering of the foggy lens of superstition, Newton swung the biggest hammer.

The new glasses Newton gave us seemed to resolve the world into sharp relief. Every high school physics book opens with his laws. You may remember the diagrams of balls being dropped, cannons being shot, and boxes being pulled up ramps. Force, mass, acceleration, velocity. Newton defined the terms and then told us how they're all connected.

We've been using his laws ever since. We used them to put a man on the moon and his best friend Rover on Mars. They are at the center of a description of the world that has come to be known as classical physics.

But they don't reflect ultimate reality. Not even a little.

This was discovered in the early 1900s by another man you'll find loitering near the top of those greatest scientist lists. Einstein idolized Newton. But as his iconic mane proclaimed, Einstein also had an irreverent streak. When you looked through Einstein's glasses, things started blending—things that Newton, and every other sane person, had always believed were separate.

Before Einstein, there was space and time and then there were things *in* space and time. Never the twain shall commingle. But Einstein showed that space and time are not the untouchable backdrop that the old physics assumed they were—not a neutral screen that objects move across. They are more like taffy that objects plow through. Space and time are squeezed and stretched by the objects moving through them. The bigger and faster the object, the greater the warp.

Einstein blended other things. He revealed that not only are objects consorting with space and time, but space and time are not such strangers either. Though in polite society, they appear to have nothing in common, Einstein realized they are best thought of as a single medium called space-time. He also realized that, behind the closed doors of what we're normally able to perceive, energy and matter were whispering $E=mc^2$ to each other. They are secret lovers, two hearts beating as one, two forms of the same thing.

Einstein's insights govern the very large. Quantum physics, another theory that arose in the early 1900s, governs the very small. Whatever of normal, Newtonian physics that remained standing after Einstein, quantum physics demolished.

Quantum physics tells us that really small things aren't necessarily things at all. At the level of atoms, particles don't always act like particles. They seem to be more fundamentally waves. If that sounds ridiculous, then you agree with the physicists who developed the theory.

But the math, every experiment conceived to test it, and the microchip-based digital revolution we live in, all vouch for it. Tiny things like electrons, which make up everything in the universe, can be spread out in a wave—in many places at once, or nowhere, depending on your interpretation. Then when we observe them, they suddenly become particles. (Yes, you heard that right. And no, we don't know how.) The motion of these "particles" bears no resemblance to the movement described by classical physics—that physics we're used to and that Newton described. Small things like electrons can instantaneously disappear and then instantaneously pop up somewhere else. Physics had taken acid.

Knowledge by Approximation

If we've known about the weirdness of relativity and quantum mechanics for a hundred years, why do we brainwash every high school senior into believing we live in Newton's commonsense classical reality? It may be for the same mix of vague reasons we send kids to high school in the first place. It's what we deem them ready for. It's simpler. It's what we've always done. And also, to be fair, classical physics works.

Sometimes.

Newton's laws are helpful for a lot of practical, obvious, everyday things. They help you chart the course of a ball you throw, a bridge you build, or a rocket you launch. But just as high school is not the real world, high school physics is not real reality.

Classical physics only seemed to be real reality, for the couple of centuries after Newton, because people didn't experience the extreme situations where its laws no longer work. But Einstein realized that those laws break down when things get enormous or fast, and quantum physicists realized they break down when things get tiny. There were parts of the reality room that humans hadn't noticed before. There even seemed to be whole other rooms. Or more poetically, "In my Father's house are many mansions."

In the twentieth century, we started peeking into the other parts of our Father's house—even walking around in them a bit. We started going to those extremes where other realities seem to be operating.

We noticed for example that Mercury is close enough to the extremely massive sun that this innermost planet feels a warping of space-time extreme enough to notice. So, while Newton's equations work well enough to predict the orbits of the other planets, you have to switch to Einstein's equations for Mercury. GPS satellites are at extreme enough heights above the earth and moving at extreme enough speeds that we have to use relativity to sync up their time with the time in our cars. And we have to use the equations of quantum physics for the extremely small guts of all our electronic devices, as well as to understand the extremely small atoms whose behavior underlies all of chemistry.

By the 1940s, the French philosopher Maurice Merleau-Ponty could report that "scientists have gotten used to the idea that their laws and theories… constitute knowledge by approximation." By then, physicists knew that not only was classical physics different from general relativity and quantum physics, but general relativity and quantum physics were also different from each other. In everyday classical physics, solid objects move in smooth predictable paths through absolute and unchanging time and space. In general relativity, objects warp the time and space around them, which in turn affects the objects. In quantum physics, objects aren't even objects. They only appear to be when they pop up here and there out of the more consistent reality of their probability waves, whatever those are.

All this shifting of gears from one reality to another may seem a ridiculous condition for a scientific discipline to be in. But maybe it also has a familiar feel. The rules of physics, after all, are a lot like human rules. They depend on where you are. You act differently in the boardroom than you do in the bedroom. Or, at least, you really should. Similarly, modern physicists use one set of rules when talking about the motion of baseballs, another set when talking about planets, and still another for electrons. Each set of rules is radically different from the others. To go from one reality mansion to another, physicists don't just change hats, they change their entire wardrobe.

But we wanted an outfit we can wear all the time. We wanted principles that apply in our Father's whole house, not the local laws in this or that mansion. We didn't ask, "What are some different areas of reality?" We asked, "What is *reality*?"

And now we know the official answer. Our modern high priests, from the great columned halls of academia, their textbooks piled high around them, the latest experimental apparatus in the lab next door, in deep and solemn tones, announce to the waiting world, "Um…"

Catch a physicist a little tipsy at a cocktail party and she might beckon you, drink-in-hand, to a corner of the living room and confide something else to you. All of the realities her colleagues have discovered—all those baseballs, planets, and electrons and all their energy, forces, and probability waves; everything they've ever described from Isaac Newton to Stephen Hawking—only make up about five percent of what what's really out there in the universe.

It turns out that certain aspects of the large-scale behavior of the universe don't make sense if regular matter and energy are all there is. To account for this behavior, physicists hypothesize some different kinds of matter and energy—kinds that no one has ever had any direct experience with (as far as they know). All physicists can say is that some other kinds of matter and energy must exist. They even gave them cool Star Wars names: *Dark Matter* and *Dark Energy*. Physicists tell us that these Darth Vader twins make up ninety-five percent of the universe.

And we know nothing about them.

Ninety-five percent of a room is a big area not to have looked for a mouse in. And if the mind-bending truths of relativity and quantum physics are anything to go by, a reasonable hypothesis would be that there are some very unreasonable things there.

An Experience Filter

In his book *The God Delusion*, Richard Dawkins argues that believing in God is silly. He doesn't mention that quantum mechanics—the most successful theory in the history of physics and the foundation of the digital era—is silly too. As an Oxford biology professor, Dawkins must at least have a general sense of the shenanigans going on a few buildings over in the theoretical physics department. Still, he wrote his book. Does he know something we don't?

One thing he'd know, were he to read this essay, is that nothing I've said is proof of any kind of divinity. He might instead classify this essay as wobbly conjecture, devoid of that essential element that forms the foundation of Science—the element that allows Science to build, brick by brick, its temples of real knowledge.

This element is widely touted by scientists as what distinguishes their humble profession from that of poets, philosophers, and mystics. Unlike art and religion, so the thinking goes, Science is honest. Science can't just say things it thinks might be true or that sound good. It doesn't make claims based on human bias, desire, or whim. It doesn't rest on the swamp of imagination. Science rests on the bedrock of evidence.

Evidence is why Science is qualified to tell us what reality is, even if it hasn't discovered all of it yet. Evidence is what has led us to all the successful theories Science has so far revealed. Evidence is what allows those theories to yield the incredible technology we all enjoy. Evidence is the ground of truth. No evidence, no reality.

Swing low, sweet evidence! We can put our faith in Science because we can put our faith in evidence. It's a compelling sermon. But one that deserves as much scrutiny as the fire-and-brimstone sermons of old. Unlike our superstitious ancestors, we no longer go glassy-eyed and turn off our brains when we hear the word *God*. Why would we do the same thing when we hear the word *evidence*?

We've seen how words can mesmerize—how hard and shiny they can seem. We've seen how easy it is to think a word we're tossing around has a definition everyone agrees on. What happens if we toss the word *evidence* around? Will it hold up like a solid ball, or start to come apart in our hands?

What do scientists mean by evidence?

Do they simply mean human experience? Yesterday I had some human experience. I felt blissful as I walked along the Carquinez Straits near my Bay Area home at sunset. There was a glow in the air. Later, I dreamed I was playing basketball with an amorphous ball and inept teammates. Was my bliss, the glow, the dream, evidence?

It's not just me. There are seven billion and counting different human experiences going on right now and all of them will have changed by the time you finish this sentence. Is that whole massive mess of shifting experience evidence?

Experience is a bigger word than *evidence*. Too big for Science. To capture all of human experience, everyone would have to constantly send "Science" their experience moment by moment, including their experience of sending in their experience, and the scientists themselves would have to do the same, except they'd have to include their experience of recording everyone's experience, including their own. This is a tall order, even for Elon Musk.

So scientists need a filter—something that allows in only some of that kaleidoscopic flood of billions of experiences that are washing, or have ever washed, over humanity. As the physicists Brian Cox and Jeff Forshaw write, "We have to draw the line somewhere in order to answer any questions at all." What gets through this "science filter" is what scientists mean by evidence.

What is the nature of this filter? What counts as evidence amidst the onslaught of experience? Often what counts is what can be counted—how many meters, grams, or wavelengths can be assigned to a phenomenon. But when something—say a bird's mating behavior—resists measurement, scientists accept qualitative description as evidence as well. What criteria do scientists apply to all observations in order for them to matter? Whether they're recording numbers or descriptions, Richard Dawkins and most scientists would probably say that real evidence—the kind that makes up real reality—is something like 'the experience that sane humans would agree they invariably have under the same conditions.'

Still Crazy

Our word *evidence* has led to yet more qualifications—more words. And it's tempting again to take all these new words at face value. It's tempting to assume that we know what they mean. It's tempting to assume that since we've never stopped to think about them before, there's no need to start doing that now.

But if we're to believe that Science can weigh in on God because it describes reality, we need to know how Science comes up with its picture of reality. And if its picture of reality is based on evidence, we need to know what Science's idea of evidence is. And if evidence is 'the experience that sane humans would agree they invariably have under the same conditions,' we need to know, among other things, what *sane* means.

Am I just nitpicking now? Aren't sane people simply all of us folks who aren't in those asylums for non-sane folks? Will this maze of words never end?

This essay does have an end. Just not here. For the "crazy" label doesn't come inscribed on an amulet and get dropped from the sky around the necks of the unfortunate nutters among us. It comes from people. Flawed people. People who may themselves be crazy. It's not at all clear that the majority in a culture always have the sane view. For much of human—including American—history, the view held by the most respected pillars of society has been that women are incapable of offering the culture much beyond tips for a really flaky biscuit. (Which is not in any way to diminish the importance of a good biscuit.) It's not even clear that most people in today's culture have a sane view. Eckhart Tolle doesn't think so. His definition of a sane person is someone who isn't identified with the thoughts and emotions that constantly stream through them, inducing a kind of trance-like state he calls insane.

You may or may not agree with that. But it's certainly true that shifting cultural ideas have a powerful effect on what gets called *sanity*. In our culture, if you tell someone you've heard voices or seen an apparition, for example, your sanity comes under question. But as Oliver Sacks points out in his book *Hallucinations*, hearing non-physical voices, as well as seeing non-physical things, is not at all uncommon among perfectly sane people, who are usually understandably reluctant to discuss their experiences. Anthony Hopkins,

Sigmund Freud, Charles Dickens, Socrates, and Mahatma Gandhi have all reported hearing voices. A friend of mine was guided to safety out of the World Trade Center on 9/11 by a voice, a detail she left out when interviewed by reporters. The similar experiences of millions of others doubtless fly under the mainstream cultural radar. Gandhi's voice also gave guidance. He said, "I have no… evidence to convince the skeptic. He is free to say that it was all self-delusion or hallucination… But I can say this, that not the unanimous verdict of the whole world against me could shake me from the belief that what I heard was the true Voice of God."

Consider how Gandhi's attitude resonates with that of tribal or "superstitious" cultures. In those societies, you'd be advised not to ignore but to listen closely to your voices and to seriously consider your apparitions. You might be considered not crazy but gifted. Your capacity to perceive such things might not be deadened by drugs but encouraged by questions. You might learn to navigate the world you'd discovered for the benefit of yourself and your tribe. This is, after all, what Gandhi did.

What is considered sane by a culture has a chance to be amplified by practice. You see more of it because you see more of it. What is considered insane is inhibited by discouragement. You see less of it because you see less of it. And if you do see it, you discount it. The "sane" part of Science's evidence filter is a cultural and therefore subjective criterion—a judgment call. Does Richard Dawkins make that call for you? The pope? Your dad? A committee of psychiatrists with golf club memberships and two mortgages?

A Hobgoblin

But what if we assume there is some absolute standard of sanity? There isn't. But what if we imagine there is (there isn't) and our scientists are darn close to models of this perfect state? Would their filter for human experience allow the most important bits to come through and be counted as evidence?

It depends on what you mean by important. What Science deems important is captured by three more words in our working definition of scientific evidence—*agree, invariably,* and *same.* In the tsunami of seven billion human experiences, scientific evidence is only what is shared by others and repeatable.

Science insists on consistency.

In the conventional scientific view of the world, to be real is to be consistent; and to be consistent is to be real. Even the idea of sanity is fundamentally an issue of consistency disguised as one of truth. We can claim the insane live in a false reality, but since no one knows what true reality is, it's more accurate to say they live in a reality that is inconsistent with that of the majority.

Science has glued the words *real* and *consistent* together—hasn't seen that they are two things. A more truly scientific approach would be more precise. It would recognize that the consistent parts of our experience are just that—the consistent parts. Useful to notice and isolate but with no claim to a grander title.

To be fair, calling Science useful is like calling The Beatles a good band. Insisting on consistency was a hugely productive idea. Filtering out all the unpredictable, individual, idiosyncratic aspects of human experience has allowed Science to do amazing, consistent things, usually involving metal and plastic. We can make factories, fridges, cars, computers, bombs, and bridges. It's dazzling.

But to be dazzled by something is usually to be blinded to something else. Imagining Science can make pronouncements about reality is not to see that Science's laws are based on an anemic slice of human experience—the slice that lots of people with PhDs agree is there on a dependable basis. Other things aren't really there…Other things aren't really there…Other things aren't really there.

Alas, saying something over and over doesn't make it true. Regardless of what the laws of Science keep saying, there are a lot of "other things" out there, even if we don't count the voices and visions we've agreed to call crazy.

What are these other things?

Everything. All the time. You may have noticed. Our moment-to-moment experience never exactly repeats itself. It is consistently inconsistent. What we see, hear, smell, taste, think, feel, and dream all flit through, float by, punch, caress, and soak us like a slapstick comedy routine. The scientific representation of reality ignores the most in-your-face aspect of human experience.

Scientific atheists fix their eyes on only the consistent elements in the human comedy routine—what stays around until the next day, week, year, century; what can be discussed with others using concrete words or, better yet, numbers; what can be written down in those words and numbers. The rest doesn't make it into the final report. The rest isn't, in the end, important.

But a lot of us would say that the rest is exactly what's most important—the beautiful moment, the blissful feeling, the nameless waters of a potent dream, the plot twist, the punchline, the highlight, the surprise, the inspiration. Ralph Waldo Emerson believed these inconsistent fairies can get spooked when the "hobgoblin" of consistency comes lumbering along. "With consistency," he wrote, "a great soul has simply nothing to do."

This is not to say Pinker or any other scientist is a soulless robot. Pinker, on the contrary, is a passionate advocate for kindness. That passion—the fire that fueled his book—is beautiful, irrational, and inconsistent.

To extract only those elements of our experience that are helpful in making an iPhone or an air conditioner and tape the label "real" on them is a human decision. A decision we've become used to. A habit. We're used to imagining our iPhones are more real than our dreams. Our dreams, after all, dissipate mist-like when we awaken, whereas the iPhone is still there on the table. Our dreams slip through our fingers when we try to describe them to a friend, whereas the iPhone has attributes we can speak in words and numbers—a color, a model, so many megabytes of storage.

But is this right? Is your iPhone more real or simply more durable than your dreams? Is it more real or simply more describable to friends? Is it more real or just more consistent?

No priest or scientist is more qualified to answer those questions than you are.

Our Own World

To believe in the story that Science preaches about ultimate reality is not only to ignore the incompleteness of modern physics, Gandhi's voice of God, the visions of the multitudes, the dream you had last night, or the gut feeling you had this morning; it is also to ignore the hairy creature who licks your face when you get home from work every day.

The news that our entire body of knowledge about physics—from the electron to the galaxy—is based on five percent of the universe isn't the only humbling headline. It's likely that the entirety of human experience offers an even smaller slice of all possible experience. Which means this essay has so far been an exercise in speciesism. Or perhaps I should say humanism. It has ignored the experience of other organisms.

We know that dogs can hear and smell things all around us that we cannot perceive. We know that radio waves and tiny particles called neutrinos are swarming us in every moment, but we are oblivious to them. What different realities do our pets live in, though they walk right along beside us? What else are dogs—never mind ducks, dung beetles, and dahlias—registering in the world that humans are not? Who is to say that the way our nervous system is wired gives us anything close to a full appreciation of all that exists?

However well-meaning or smart, Steven Pinker can't have the experience of a salamander. But I can't think of a good reason why we should assume the salamander's experience is trivial. The only logic behind omitting the salamander's experience from our official reality report is that we haven't heard from any salamanders.

And if we did? If we collected reports from all the species of the planet? If we tried to overcome every objection and omission in our reality report? Would we then have—at least in theory—a full picture of reality?

No. As biological creatures, we are trapped inside our subjective interpretation of the world around us. Everything we know about "out there" comes to us through our senses and is experienced "in here." That goes for a salamander as well as for a scientist.

Take the smell of coffee. What does that subjective experience—that delicious, indescribable aroma—correspond to in the objective world? According to Science, it corresponds to molecules of a particular shape. That's it—molecules. It is we humans who transform those boring molecules into the incredible fragrance of coffee. The molecules land on receptors in our nose which causes a nerve signal to be sent to our brain where somehow that electrical signal is experienced as something wondrous.

Similarly, scientists tell us that what we experience as different colors is, out there in the objective world, just different wavelengths of electromagnetic energy. What we experience as blue is really light with a wavelength near 470 nanometers. What we experience as red is light with a wavelength of about 700 nanometers. Somehow that quantitative difference in the wavelengths is transformed into a qualitative difference between the experience of blue and red. The difference between the two wavelengths out there in the world is boring—two different lengths. But the difference between blue and red in our experience is exciting, graphic, indescribable, subjective.

We habitually use the word *interpret* to describe what humans do to sensory input. But that word is inadequate. It brings to mind language, the context in which *interpret* is most commonly used. "Vous allez à la maison" means "You go to the house." Words in French are interpreted into words in English. In language interpretation, you start and end with the same kind of thing: words.

This is not what happens when our biology meets the objective world. Our subjective experience is of a profoundly different nature than the objective input that triggered it. There's no rational connection between the two. "Interpreting" a molecule into the delicious smell of coffee is like "interpreting" a word into a burrito, a sentence into a swim in a lake. We don't *interpret* objective stimuli. We create something entirely new from them—something that exists in a different dimension. It's as if the objective stimuli just served as a tiny prick of inspiration for our subjective experience of it.

We are all Pablo Picasso by default. We are inherently, effortlessly, biologically creative. There's no escaping our status as artists in every moment of our experience. I'm reminded of the words of a certain poet. "Reality is not what it is. It consists of the many realities that it can be made into."

Filling in Blanks

The young woman in Pinker's audience was one of many intelligent people who go to Science to break spells. All the spells. Once and for all. To finally see the landscape of reality clearly. And then to look in that landscape for a reason for living.

Pinker's book makes a convincing argument that our body of scientific knowledge is humanity's greatest achievement of the last three hundred years. It's right to celebrate that achievement deep into the night.

But in the morning, there's a hangover. To sober up is to realize that the achievements of Science are practical, not spiritual. Like every human enterprise, Science is limited in scope. Like every human enterprise—including art and religion—it takes place against a backdrop of mystery that it can gesture at but never plumb. It sheds its light within one mansion in our Father's house, but cannot see the whole house. Even the mansion it has illuminated—with its warped space-time and electrons popping out of nebulous waves— challenges the rationality Science is based on.

Science is a tool, not an answer. It can be used to make a nuclear bomb or a nuclear power plant, a machine gun or a sewing machine. If Science were the answer, then scientists would be the happiest people on the planet. But where's the lever you pull to make someone fall in love with you? What chapter in a textbook tells you how to have a meaningful life?

Pinker reports surprising himself with his spontaneous answer to the young woman's question. Why should she live? Because, he says, she's been endowed with reason. And because she can flourish by refining that reason through science, by using that reason to gain insight into the human condition through the arts and humanities, by enjoying herself, by noticing beauty, and by giving others what she expects for herself.

Pinker was pleased with his answer. But I imagine the young woman leaving the talk feeling bleaker for it. I imagine she had gone to the well of the oracle and it had come up dry. I imagine she feels like I feel. If my inner life is nothing but the crackling of neurons creating the impression of a soul destined to disappear for eternity when the calories run out, then words about reason, beauty, and kindness ring hollow. I imagine her gazing on the blank backdrop of Science's vision of the universe, and I imagine Pinker offering her a pencil.

I imagine what she wants is a paintbrush.

III. What You See Is What You See
Common Sense & Ultimate Truth

"The greatest obstacle to discovery is not ignorance—
it is the illusion of knowledge."
—Daniel J. Boorstein

My friend Paul, now in his fifties, has lost both his parents. He was especially close to his mother, who died from a brain tumor when Paul was seventeen. She was our music teacher in middle school. She loved kids. Everybody loved her. She suffused Paul's home with a deep sweetness I felt every time I went there. Since then, Paul has felt her absence almost every day.

Paul doesn't just feel her absence. He knows her absence. Knows it as a fact: his mother isn't there. Worse, he doesn't think she's anywhere. When I asked Paul what he thinks happens after we die, he said, "Nothing. How could it be otherwise?" To Paul, and to many intelligent people like him, the absence of those who have passed on, and the finality of that passing, are obvious. As much as we'd like to believe something else, a rational appraisal of the human condition won't allow it. We can't see how it could be otherwise.

There was a time when most humans believed in otherwise. The other world—below, above, beyond, around—was taken for granted. The spirits of ancestors were consulted, fed, and danced for. Gods, ghosts, and angels were real. But this spiritual neighborhood began losing credibility as reason began gaining it. Or so the standard story goes. In 1882 it became official. "God," said the German philosopher Friedrich Nietzsche, "is dead."

And Science seemed to be holding the machine gun.

Nietzsche's century had witnessed an unprecedented explosion of technology, from the machine gun itself, to factories, steam engines, electric lights, and telephones. To Nietzsche and many of his contemporaries, it was obvious that the juggernaut of the modern world was not fed by manna from heaven, but by inventions from humans. And thanks to Darwin, the origin of those humans had been downgraded from theological to just plain logical. You could go on entertaining fantasies if you wanted, but in the real world, reason trumped religion. Whether you were reading the Torah, the Koran, or the Gospel According to Mark, gravity was holding you to your chair. Like the other laws of Science, you don't get to believe in gravity or not. It's what's for breakfast.

Today, a lot of intelligent people accept that plate of cold eggs. They believe they live in a world that is ultimately mechanical and therefore ultimately meaningless. We can believe a comforting story only if we deny common sense. We can't have both. Science won't allow it.

Educated Guess

Most people—at least in the developed West—believe even more bad news. In a 2014 survey, ninety-five percent of Americans and Europeans said they thought the world was getting worse instead of better. Isn't it obvious? Bitter, partisan politics; school shootings; global warming; floods and hurricanes; imminent crises of all manner.

But our ideas about reality and reality itself are in this instance different things. By almost every measure of material well-being, data shows the world has been getting substantially better. Almost everywhere, people are richer, healthier, freer, and better educated than they've been in the past. Hunger, for example, was ubiquitous for much of human history—even in nineteenth century Europe—and famines commonplace. No longer. In 2008, the population of the entire planet had an average income equal to that of Western Europe in 1964. The percentage of those living in extreme poverty has fallen from 37% in 1990 to 10% in 2017. The number of women who die in childbirth has dropped from almost 1 out of 100 births in 1900, to 1 out of 10,000 today. In 1960, 42% of the world could read. In 2015, 86% could. More people have access to clean water, social equality is on the rise, diseases have been eradicated, people live longer, and on and on.

What may be especially surprising is that since 1980 the world has also gotten 14% greener. That's not a joke. Nor do I have a shoebox stuffed with cash from Chevron in my freezer. This increase in vegetation is most likely due to higher carbon dioxide concentrations in the atmosphere. Many don't realize that, despite its reputation as the antichrist, CO_2 is plant food. It provides the carbon atoms that build plants and every other living thing. In more environmental news, deforestation in richer countries has been declining for centuries, while tropical deforestation has been declining for the last few decades. The Environmental Performance Index, which scores countries on the quality of their air, water, natural habitats, farms, and fisheries, has risen for 178 of the 180 countries it tracks.

If all this good news has an unreal feel, it's likely because we're not used to hearing it. We hear bad news every day. News agencies comb the planet in search of the most alarming events—or potential events—they can find and push them onstage before us. Framed by the curtains of pedigreed news agencies, accompanied by colorful graphics and grand music, it makes a convincing show. Like the latest Netflix drama, it gets talked about with friends. Those conversations further reinforce its reality. Like the strictly mechanical rules of science, the decline of the world becomes what's for breakfast. Normal and therefore obvious. Obvious and therefore true.

It is normal. And it is obvious. But it's not true.

Could other obvious things also be wrong? What of the finality of death? What of a cold, uncaring universe that people like my friend Paul believe they have to accept if they want to continue being intelligent?

Hidden Order

To believe that what's obvious is what's true is to be in good company. Our first scientist believed it too. During Greece's Golden

Age, around 330 BC, Aristotle took a sober look at the world around him and drew some commonsense conclusions.

At the foundation of Aristotle's beliefs about the universe sat an earth that was stationary. How could it be otherwise? Unless you'd been partying with Socrates (who, it was said, could drink anyone under the table), no one had to steady themselves when they stood up. When it came to the stuff on this stationary earth, it was clear to Aristotle that there were four basic kinds of it—stuff made of fire, air, water, and earth. The things made of fire and air rise away from the earth and the things made of earth and water fall towards it. Of those falling things, the heavier ones fall faster than the lighter ones. Celestial things, like the sun and planets, clearly follow different rules. Instead of moving in straight lines towards the earth, they move in circles around it.

Those ideas sounded good to people. So good that they went unquestioned for about two thousand years. They were approved of by the Catholic Church and taught in the finest medieval universities by the brightest academic minds.

And as you probably know, they are all wrong.

That Aristotle's ideas were believed for so long is understandable. Not only did they have official sponsorship, they seemed obvious to the casual observer. Along with the ground appearing to stay where it was, everybody saw the sun coming up and moving across the sky. If you didn't care that much about such things, you could say, "Yeah. Definitely. The sun's moving around us. In pretty much a circle." When someone dropped a leaf and a rock, you'd notice the rock hit the ground first. "Looks like heavier things fall faster. How about a sandwich?"

Though Aristotle's framework for viewing the world had been poked here and there by inquiring minds, it started getting pulverized in the sixteenth century. The first wrecking ball was the 1543 publication of *On the Revolutions of Celestial Spheres,* in which Copernicus proposed that it only seems like the sun is moving around us. In reality, we're moving around the sun. A few decades later, Johannes Kepler calculated that the orbits are only roughly circular. To be more precise, they're ovals. Galileo believed that, despite all the fluttering leaves and plummeting rocks, lighter things fall just as fast as heavier ones—as long as you correct for air resistance. In about 1590, so the legend goes, he dropped two balls of different weights off the Leaning Tower of Pisa and proved his counterintuitive hunch. One by one, over the next three hundred years, scores of scientists would discover that the essential elements of the stuff around us were not earth, air, fire, and water. They were phosphorous (1669), platinum (1735), nickel (1751), oxygen (1774) and so on. The number of elements turns out not to be an obvious bet like four, but a number no one would have put their money on: 118. The Scientific Revolution was under way.

Its new sheriff was Isaac Newton, still widely considered the greatest scientist who ever lived. Unlike Aristotle, Newton didn't need the pope for a sidekick. He had a new weapon in his holster: equations. Where Aristotle and the church had offered loose collections of observations, Newton gave us a system of rigorous, mathematical laws. Published in 1687, these laws seemed to describe almost all the motion in the Universe. The Christ-like grandeur of his achievement inspired Alexander Pope's epitaph, "Nature and Nature's laws lay hid in night:/ God said, Let Newton be! and all was light."

But while the words *system, rigorous, mathematical,* and *laws* suggest a march towards common sense, Newton's light often revealed a weirder world than the one Aristotle saw.

Despite, for example, Aristotle's commonsense notion that celestial objects follow different rules from earthly ones, Newton's math said otherwise. The moon orbiting the earth is abiding by the same gravitational formula as a rock falling straight towards it. One rock circles. The other plummets. Same law.

Newton's math revealed yet more order that had been "hid in night." The spectacle of everyday experience would have us believe that once you get something moving, it always eventually stops. This goes for levers you pull, balls you throw, and cars you drive. If you want to keep something going, you have to keep pushing or pulling it. But that only appears to be true. Newton's first law of motion states that moving objects tend to stay moving. It turns out that all those objects we think are slowing down on their own are being acted on by a ghost named Friction.

Newton's third law is less obvious still. It insists that stationary, inanimate objects can apply forces. When you put a book on a table, the table pushes up on the book. Constantly. Without getting tired. (If it didn't, gravity would pull the book down... down... down...)

Not only that, but the table is also discerning. If you put a cinder block next to the book, the table pushes the cinder block with a different force than it's using on the book. Tables only look lazy and stupid.

Like the state of the world getting worse, Aristotle's ideas were obvious. And wrong. The laws proposed after him—by Copernicus, Kepler, Galileo, Newton, and others—were less obvious. And more right.

Reality had to be probed, studied, paid attention to, in order to give up its secrets. It seems that Heraclitus, another Greek philosopher, may have gotten closer to the truth more than a hundred years before Aristotle with his own version of a law: "Nature loves to hide."

Groovy Truth

Aristotle's laws were like the costume of Science. They looked good and didn't offend anyone. Newton's laws, on the other hand, worked. Along with the equations of electricity later unveiled by James Maxwell, you could use them to predict the behavior of artillery shells, pistons, gears, and light bulbs. The math, and the machinery that paraded from it, were so impressive that by the time Nietzsche wrote his obituary for God, it seemed that Nature was done hiding. Surely, she now stood naked before us in all her mechanical, Godless glory.

This is the world we seem to live in today—the one that now seems like common sense. Some of its features may be hard to see at first, but once learned, its laws are logical and mechanical. Which means they seem to rule out the possibility of some kind of God, some kind of meaning, some kind of hope for my friend that he will ever see his mother again.

Like the stationary earth of old, this world feels like solid ground. Its rules feel so apparent, they aren't usually considered rules, but simply reality. Too obvious to point out.

Imagine your impatience, for example, if a friend informed you that space and time are two different things. "Thank you, Sherlock," you might be tempted to reply, "That's sort of why I measure the length of my couch with a tape measure and not a stopwatch." Say

Captain Obvious felt like continuing and pointed out that, speaking of couches, the size of your furniture has no effect on how quickly time moves in your living room. Failing to interpret your blank stare, he then knocks on your kitchen table and announces that it's a solid object because it's made of a whole bunch of solid little particles. As you grab your coat, perhaps he advises that if you ever want to relocate that table to the other side of the kitchen, you'll have to move it across the space in between. Because, did you know, it can't just disappear and instantaneously appear somewhere else. Finally, as you're running out the door, he shouts after you, "Don't worry! Your table will still be in the kitchen when you're not here to observe it!

We aren't interested in what we take for granted. All your friend's observations in the scenario above are so ingrained in how we operate that discussing them feels trivial. They are basic to how we perceive reality. They were the invisible assumptions of the Scientific Revolution, Newton's laws, Darwin's theory of evolution, and all the inventions that led Nietzsche to announce that God had kicked the cosmic bucket. We've built bridges, factories, cars, and rockets with them.

But when it comes to ultimate reality, all the obvious things your friend droned on about are—like the world getting worse and Aristotle's commonsense notions—once again, wrong. This time, I'm tempted to say wrong with a capital W. But they don't make letters big enough for how wrong our everyday conception of reality is.

There has been a new sheriff in town for over a hundred years now. Everybody knows his name, but few know that by 1915, he had run Newton out of town. His only sidekick seemed to be Lewis Carroll. Albert Einstein ushered in another revolution whose Alice-in-Wonderland implications for the nature of reality make those of the Scientific Revolution look quaint. They are so bizarre that even after more than a century, they are simply not on the radar of most intelligent people.

When Einstein started daydreaming about light around 1905, its essential nature was considered settled. It was a wave. After all, for the last hundred years, scientists had seen overwhelming evidence of it acting like one. But about the time Nietzsche was making his grandiose claim of divine demise, scientists were being humbled by a couple of situations in which light refused to behave like a good little wave. One phenomenon was deemed so inappropriate it was dubbed the "ultraviolet catastrophe."

Einstein's solution was nonsensical. Despite all the evidence that light was a wave, he proposed that on some occasions light was a particle. Or at least acted like a particle. To understand light, sometimes we have to picture it as a wave and sometimes we have to picture it as a particle. This has become the currently accepted view, what physicists call light's "particle-wave duality."

It is not how anything in our commonsense world works. Imagine standing in the surf and closing your eyes as the waves wash gently around you. Suddenly the ocean goes flat, and the waves become a big rubber ball that smacks you in the face. That's about the size of it. Light is two radically different things at the same time—something our brains say is impossible. A particle is an inert object; a wave is spread-out energy. A particle is a wave? You may as well say an elephant is a song.

To say light is two radically different things at the same time is to say we don't know what it is. We can only grasp what we experience every day. On no day do we experience something that is both a wave and a particle. Our minds can't imagine it. And, according to scientists, it's absolutely true.

Einstein had more nonsensical news to report in 1905. Like a lunatic, his theory of special relativity babbled that space and time are not absolute. They squeeze and stretch depending on how fast you're going. They do this even though no one has ever experienced them doing it. Furthermore, it said $E=mc^2$, which is math for "Energy and matter are the same thing." That's like saying movement is the same thing as the object that moves. What is the single 'thing' that energy and matter both are? Nobody knows. We sane people experience matter and energy only as two different things.

Einstein wasn't done raving. His General Theory of Relativity, completed in 1915, did away entirely with a cornerstone of physics for hundreds of years—Newton's idea of gravity. Einstein's math was as logical as Newton's, but its conclusions about reality sounded even more implausible. Gravity was not a force between objects; it was a warping of *space-time*. According to General Relativity, space and time are not separate. They are blended in a kind of silly putty everything moves through. Objects bend this space-time around them. The bigger the object, the greater the bend. Planets orbit the sun because it bends the space-time around it. You and I stay on the ground because the bent space-time around the earth is pushing us here.

Einstein wrote that "There is no logical way to the discovery of these elemental laws. There is only the way of intuition, which is helped by a feeling for the order lying behind the appearance." Einstein saw truth, but not with his eyes. He saw unobvious truth. He confirmed in spades those words of Heraclitus. "Nature loves to hide."

Modern technology—able to perceive what we cannot—has since verified Einstein's inner visions. Really weird things are really true.

Was Einstein the first hippie? His physics anticipated psychedelia by fifty years. Since he died in 1955, we'll never know if he approved of his flower children. We do know that he disapproved of another child of his: Quantum Physics. It was too weird, even for Einstein.

Particles Wave

Quantum physics is the study of the extremely small. It's a description of what physicists have found as they've dived deeper and deeper into the stuff around us—into the atoms that everything is made of. It emerged in the early 1900s in the wake of Einstein's radical new ideas and has been elaborated on by many brilliant minds continuously to the present day. It's officially known as quantum *mechanics*, which seems odd given that the theory lays waste to a mechanistic view of the world. But if the name makes little sense, the theory makes none.

Not even to the physicists who formulated it. One of those physicists, Nobel-prize winner Richard Feynman, is said to have quipped, "If you think you understand quantum mechanics, you don't understand quantum mechanics." The concepts we get from everyday experience—the building blocks of how we think and understand—don't apply. According to many quantum physicists, the only authentic response to the truths they've discovered is to be baffled.

Quantum physics tells us that it isn't just light that is both a particle and a wave. Everything is. Electrons, protons, atoms, molecules, chairs, cars, planets, and you.

Everything we call an object has a wave associated with it—even somehow *is* that wave. Physicists call it a probability wave. The smaller the particle, the bigger the wave. The bigger the particle, the smaller the wave. That's why we can be forgiven for not noticing these waves before. Everyday objects like chairs and cars are big enough things that their probability waves are too tiny for humans to detect. It was only as physicists developed the technology to look at tiny things that the probability waves became big enough to notice.

What is a probability wave? In one sense it's clear. It has a definite mathematical formula. But what it is in the real world is hard for us humans to grasp—and may even be ungraspable. Is it a real thing? Or is it just information *about* a thing? Probability waves are like nothing we've ever encountered or heard of. They don't tell us where something is, but where we are likely to find it.

Take electrons, which are one of the three tiny particles inside all atoms, which themselves make up all matter around us. According to overwhelming scientific evidence, electrons only sometimes act like little rocks or bullets with definite locations. At other times, they are somehow embodied in a wave of probability. Where an electron's probability wave is high, you're likely to find the electron associated with that wave. But you cannot say for certain where you will find it. An electron can somehow potentially exist at many places with different probabilities. Same for the protons and neutrons in atoms. Which means, same for the atom itself. And since everything is made of atoms, same for you and everything around you.

In our everyday lives we experience particles, not probability waves. This may lead you to wonder why or how a probability wave becomes a particle. Nobody knows. Physicists can't explain what they refer to as the "collapse" of the probability wave. They don't know why or how a spread-out wave of probable existence collapses into a solid particle in one place. They can only say *when* it happens.

When we look at it.

The crash you just heard is the toppling of a central pillar of common sense and of how we think of Science itself. The world, according to quantum physics, is not objective. When we observe it, we affect it.

No one understands how our everyday reality of dependable, solid-seeming objects arises from this quantum reality. When are things real and when are they not? Do you exist before I observe you? Or vice versa? Can the glance of a dog or an ant convert a wave to a particle?

* * *

Like the reality of a world getting dramatically better, the truths of quantum physics are so far from our everyday experience that they don't register. They play no role in how almost everyone, including my friend Paul, thinks about what's ultimately true. They are, effectively, not real.

But really? They are real. Really real. In fact, the theory of quantum mechanics is widely regarded by physicists as the most successful theory in the history of science. Yes, it's silly. Yes, it suggests that the reality underlying our everyday lives is utterly unlike what we experience in those everyday lives. Yes, it makes no sense. But over and over, no matter how ridiculous its predictions, decades of incredibly accurate experiments have testified to its truth. In the words of MIT physicist, Seth Lloyd, "There are literally billions of pieces of confirming evidence for quantum mechanics."

It's not just in the lab. It's in the real world. It's likely in your pocket or purse or palm right now. It's why we have the micro-chip, and thus cell phones, computers, and everything else digital. As Oberlin physicist Dan Styer writes, quantum mechanics also "underlies our understanding of atoms, molecules, solids, and nuclei. It is vital for explaining aspects of stellar evolution, chemical reactions, and the interaction of light with matter. It underlies the operation of lasers, transistors, magnets, and superconductors." Our knowledge of quantum mechanics, in other words, explains the behavior of all the particles everything is made of, and has made modern life possible.

The weirdest theory ever conceived is also the truest and most useful.

How can physicists use a theory that they fundamentally don't understand? The same way I flip a switch and get light without being able to explain the electrical system in my house. The same way Newton offered us an equation to calculate gravity without knowing what gravity was. The same way that for eons the sun gave life to humans without requiring analysis. We don't have to understand in order to benefit.

* * *

Before quantum mechanics, when physicists strolled casually through the world, it all looked normal. OK, maybe we thought the sun was moving when it was actually the earth. Maybe orbits looked like circles when they were really ovals. Those are fairly easy adjustments to make to our view of reality.

But beginning in the early twentieth century, when physicists got down on their knees and peered intensely at the little things that make up all the big things around us, those little things winked and turned into waves. Those little things flickered between being and not being things. Those little things that make up everything defied our most fundamental concepts of how reality behaves. The normal world we experience every day is made of a swarm of little mysteries.

Talk about Nature loving to hide.

More News

We believe we're walking through a forest of objects. Instead we're floating in a sea of vibration. This is the central revelation of quantum mechanics. Along with Einstein's discoveries, it's a big enough explosion of common sense to keep the mind bewildered for a lifetime.

But to leave off describing the fireworks that is modern physics at this point would be to sorely under-report the story. It would risk leaving you with the impression that the show was over, that you might be able to pick up the pieces of your common sense and reassemble it somehow; that there were only these few strange aspects of reality to either incorporate into your worldview or just overlook; that there was a chance ultimate truth could still resemble your everyday experience.

There isn't. To read in any depth about modern physics is to find that each absurd revelation only ignites more of them, as though each glowing trail of an explosion itself explodes into more glowing trails, and on and on, until it seems the fireworks will never end, and you simply shake your head, while you still have one, and close the book.

It's just as strange an experience to write about quantum physics. All I can do here is use words, yet none are adequate. Words unfold one at a time in a neat little line. Words are based on what we experience. For both reasons, words don't apply here. I could counsel a break from these words. Walk outside and let this stuff sink in. But it would be a long break.

A better option I think is to get some popcorn and allow yourself to be entertained as you would by a movie. Yes, this movie is technically a documentary, but there won't be any incorporating of these ideas into your worldview. What physicists have confirmed, or are conjecturing, about what's ultimately true is too far removed from anyone's worldview. Further removed than even the most outrageous fantasy movie. Yet, when you leave this theater, you won't be able to say, "That was entertaining, but let's get back to reality." This time, according to modern science, the outrageous movie is closer to actual reality than the one you want to get back to.

So what happens in the next scene? No sooner are we told that all objects are actually probability waves, than we learn that the probability wave of every particle covers the entire universe. Within this wave, in the words of authors Brian Cox and Jeff Forshaw, "a particle really can be in several places at once and moves from one place to another by exploring the entire Universe simultaneously."

That's a single particle. Like, say, an electron. Remember, electrons are one of the three particles that make up atoms, and thus make up everything in the universe—air, rocks, trees, couches, planets, stars; everything. Electrons are so small there are about 17,000 trillion in a grain of salt. The number of them in the universe is unimaginable. So is the size of the universe. I'm told that just the part we can observe is 550 million trillion miles across. And now Cox and Forshaw, two sane, tenured physics professors, are telling us that every single one of those electrons—not to mention all the other particles—are simultaneously exploring the entire universe before making the slightest move. When they do move, they could instantaneously appear anywhere.

It does not, in other words, violate the laws of physics for your table to suddenly vanish and reappear on the other side of your kitchen. Or on Mars. It's true no one has ever seen this happen. (Or if someone has, they have shrewdly kept it to themselves.) But that's not because it's impossible. It's because the probability of it happening is low. Very low. So low that it's almost always better to just get a friend to help you move it.

The parenthetical subtitle of Cox and Forshaw's book, *The Quantum Universe (and why anything that can happen, does)*, refers to this tendency of everything to go everywhere all the time. But the statement, "anything that can happen, does," could just as well also refer to another brain-shattering idea some physicists believe could explain that moment when a spread-out probability wave becomes a concrete particle in one place. The many-worlds interpretation proposes that the wave doesn't actually collapse at all. When we observe, say, an electron, we don't force it to appear as a particle in one particular spot. Or we do, but only in the universe we happen to be in. In that same instant, an immense number of other universes split off (yes, other universes), and in each one, the electron appears at a different place in its wave. One choice isn't made. All choices are made.

But remember, what applies to electrons applies to everything—you, your couch, your car, and your goldfish. For every possible version of the electron, there's a version of you seeing it. In the many-worlds view then, all of reality is branching in every instant into every possible event, each event in its own universe. Then *that* universe branches, and so on. If you believe this explanation, you'll find it either frustrating or comforting that, in some universe, you just won the lottery. In another, you won it twice in a row.

I'll give you a sec to collect the pieces of your skull.

Get some more popcorn while you're at it. This movie is yet longer and weirder. And like *Pulp Fiction*, it follows many plots. In one, proponents of something called string theory argue that there aren't just the three dimensions of space and one of time that we're aware of, but six more invisible dimensions. Right where you are, right now. String theory says that literally everything—all forces, energy, and particles in the universe—are composed of a variety of little strings that vibrate within ten dimensions. Like guitar strings, each plays a certain "note," which makes it look to us like a certain particle. Unlike guitar strings, they have (insanely) no width. Physicists have a mathematical model of how these strings can lead to everything around us, but there's no proof they exist, since they're so tiny they make electrons look like Mt. McKinley.

The math of string theory suggests to Stanford physicist Leonard Susskind that the universe—including you and me—is a two-dimensional hologram. Cut to England, where the Oxford physicist Roger Penrose speculates that when the universe expands to a certain immense size, it "loses track of scale, so big and small become equivalent," and it can suddenly be a tiny speck. At this point it explodes into a new universe, which expands, until it too forgets how huge it is. Not all physicists think Penrose is right. But all do accept that at the moment our universe was born, all of it was compressed to billions of times smaller than a grain of sand. If that seems a bit abstract, consider that we *have* found extremely compressed matter in today's universe, in the form of something called a neutron star. Just a teaspoon of a neutron star weighs four billion tons, and thus makes a great gag gift.

Einstein had limited tolerance for the madness he helped to spawn. Because it was a consequence of his special theory of relativity, for example, he had to accept that events one person experiences as simultaneous may not be simultaneous for someone else—depending on their speeds, their distance apart, and their distances from the events. This meant he had to stand by the assertion that the current "now" of someone somewhere in the universe could include the death of Julius Caesar. But there was much in quantum physics that Einstein couldn't stand. For starters, he wanted there to really be an objective world that exists apart from us observing it. He was also bothered by the theory's prediction that particles could instantaneously affect each other, even from opposite sides of the universe. His discomfort about the idea is clear in the name he gave it: "spooky action at a distance." About twenty-five years after his death, it was decisively proven.

If physicists were to give prizes for the most pervasive and least obvious features of reality, those probability waves of every particle extending throughout the universe make good candidates. So do neutrinos. Detected in 1959, these tiny particles are currently streaming through every man, woman, child, and eggplant at the rate of

420 billion per square inch per second. (The sun and other stars emit most of them.) It would be hard to argue, though, with awarding two first prizes to what physicists call dark energy and dark matter.

It turns out that certain aspects of how stars and galaxies move don't make sense if regular old energy and matter are all there is. Physicists therefore believe that different kinds of energy and matter must also exist. This dark energy and dark matter are different from all the light, energy, and particles they already find so baffling. Beyond "different," though, they have no idea what these other kinds of energy and matter are like. That's no idea as in literally no idea. Physicists do have an idea, though, how much of the universe must be composed of these two blind spots: ninety-five percent.

* * *

Conventional wisdom holds that math and science throw a wet blanket on the illogical and the fantastical. Yet no other discipline—not religion, philosophy, or literature—has ever offered a more preposterous affront to the human brain than the math and science that is modern physics. Our most brass-tacks, no-nonsense, what-you-see-is-what-you-get way of approaching the world has forced its practitioners to accept conclusions more outlandish than anyone else ever dreamed.

Double Homicide

Where does this all leave my friend Paul? Or anyone who wants to believe the Universe offers us more than obliteration, that it cares about what and who we love.

As you'd expect, physicists have various ideas about divinity or the lack thereof. From what I can tell, most speculate cautiously, waiting for a definitive memo from God—as long as it comes in the form of an equation. More than a few mock the wanna-be mystics who haven't mastered the math but who nevertheless claim that it all adds up to unicorns. Science writer Adam Becker warns us away from the "constant river of New Age nonsense" that is spewed in the name of quantum mechanics. The particle physicists Cox and Forshaw prefer the phrase "reams of drivel." They go on to write that while it is true that cats can be both alive and dead, and particles can be in two places at once, the conclusion that we are "steeped in mystery" is "most definitely not" true.

This last statement might be as bizarre as quantum physics itself. I don't believe in unicorns. Nor am I a fan of flowing purple robes. But having read and heard what I would unscientifically call "a lot" about quantum physics from people with Phds, my unPhd-ed conclusion is the opposite of Cox and Forshaw's. Unless the meaning of the word *mystery* was changed when I wasn't looking, we are definitely steeped in it.

But mystery is not the same as comfort. What Becker, Cox, Forshaw, and other cool-headed physicists often see as their duty is to keep us soft-hearted types from coloring in the unknown with what we want to be there. Scientists, in general, hate this. It represents a regression to the superstitious imaginings the Scientific Revolution was supposed to have demolished. Science has made the progress it has made precisely because its practitioners have not allowed themselves to conclude something just because they'd like it to be true. Scientists instead impose a discipline on themselves. They allow themselves to conclude only what is supported by the evidence. Then they look for rational, not emotional, explanations.

The paradox is that the more scientists have valued evidence, the less it seems they can trust appearances. And the deeper they dig with their rational minds, the less those rational minds can grasp what they find. I'm reminded of the black and white yin-yang symbol of Taosim. As one color swells bigger and bigger, the seed of the opposite color is found within it. And there I go, getting mystical. I hear the gnashing of the teeth of a thousand physicists.

But deeper than that, I hear a resonance of the discoveries of modern physics with a wisdom that is far from New Age. It's a wisdom that goes back millennia. It has found expression under many names and variations beyond Taoism—from Heraclitus, Socrates, and Plato in ancient Greece, to the yogis of both ancient and present-day India, from the alchemists of Europe to the Sufis of the Islamic world, from the Buddha and Christ to Emerson and Eckhart Tolle. Sometimes called the perennial philosophy, it agrees with modern physics that appearances are illusory and that what lies behind them is beyond the capacity of the rational mind.

Many in this tradition have also been saying for centuries what is arguably the most shocking discovery of modern physics—that the world is not objective; the observer affects the observed. According to ancient sources, the Buddha said, "Phenomena are preceded by the heart, ruled by the heart, made of the heart;" Heraclitus said, "Because of disbelief, it escapes being known;" and Jesus said, "Whatever you ask for in prayer, believe that you have received it, and it will be yours."

Seen in the light of the perennial philosophy, reality is an interplay—or even a blurring of the boundaries—of the outside and the inside worlds. God—or meaning or comfort—are not exactly things out there in the universe like traffic lights that send an unambiguous signal to the passive brain of any human. The inner state of the seeker matters. Powerful events like the disappearance of someone we love are not made of stone, but of clay. We make of them what we make of them. We can be wrecked or deepened. As much as life happens to us, we happen to life.

The story of physics, from Aristotle to Einstein and beyond, is the story of the inadequacy of a casual appraisal of the world. To really know reality is to dive through that veneer into a realm that is nothing like normal but that somehow gives rise to the normal around us. The master practitioners of the perennial philosophy tell us something analogous about our search for God. Just as the effect of an observer matters more at the level of tiny particles like electrons, so our participation matters more if we're looking for something deeper than traffic lights.

If this is true, then that "something deeper" cannot be handed to you by someone else the way a mathematical equation can. The poet Alfred Lord Tennyson put it this way: "Nothing worthy proving can be proven." According to this logic, it's exactly because physics lies in the realm of proof that we should not look to it for a final word on what matters most to us. Physics can't do the heavy lifting required to raise God from the grave Nietzsche dug for Him.

Neither did physics kill God. What it did was commit a different murder, every bit as momentous. It's an assassination that deserves a place in our consciousness as we contemplate what could be ultimately true. "Common sense is dead." It isn't as memorable as "God is dead." But it may be more comforting.

It is, at any rate, more accurate.

IV. Where Scientists Fear to Tread

Science, Taboos, Magic & Meaning

"Concepts that have proven useful... achieve such authority
over us that we forget their earthly origins and accept them
as unalterable givens."

—Albert Einstein

In modern intellectual culture, what's called the paranormal or supernatural is walled off in a kind of ghetto. It's a bustling and colorful neighborhood. Founders of religions, seekers of initiation, and the writers of novels, movies, and TV shows all go there for inspiration by the thousands. Everyday people who experience compelling encounters with UFOs, ghosts, angels, and all manner of strange beings suddenly find themselves there by the hundreds of thousands. The CIA has spent millions to fund expeditions there. But respectable people almost never go there.

Scientists are among the most respectable people when it comes to modern intellectual culture. We tend to look to them for the no-nonsense lowdown on what's really true. Science is Western culture's Judge Judy of reality. And Judge Judy doesn't hang out on street corners. Sure, like most of us, scientists are generally happy to smile good-naturedly from afar at the shenanigans in the ghetto—on a movie screen, say, or in the pages of a work of fiction. But try to lead them inside for a closer look and their noses start crinkling.

Many intelligent non-scientists have a similar response. There's a good chance, in fact, that having seen the words *paranormal* and *supernatural*, you're wondering if you want to keep reading this essay—as though you're standing at the gates of the ghetto wall. As you weigh the likelihood of any good coming from entering, alarms may be going off—perhaps a sense that you're about to step in something that will be hard to completely wipe off your shoes; perhaps just a vague, queasy feeling.

On the other hand, you may already live with another vague, queasy feeling—one that modern intellectual culture heartily encourages. It arises from the vision of existence endorsed by those very Judge Judys we look to for answers. It's been on the rise ever since Reason began nudging Religion off the throne of Western culture. It's behind Eliot's Wasteland, Camus's Stranger, Munch's Scream, and the blank stare of most of what fills modern art galleries. It's the feeling that partly fuels our fascination with technology, as if more gadgets might quell the queasiness. It's the nauseating hum in the background of being a smart person: Existence is meaningless and death is the end. To be sophisticated in today's culture seems to mean accepting a kind of final wall.

Don't Go There

Metaphorical walls are everywhere in the human experience. They seal off places we don't visit, either out of politeness or fear, or because we just don't think it's possible. Some walls are collective, some are personal. They change from culture to culture and from person to person. They bar us from what we should not, or cannot, talk about: our dissatisfaction with a marriage, some act of vanity, some secret pleasure, an apparition, an out-of-body experience, a fart, death. To breach a wall feels taboo.

Humans, like caged animals, tend to pace in front of walls. Walls keep us safe, but they also keep us contained. They both repel and attract. They give us pause and they entice. What's behind that thing? Maybe something we want. The paradox is inherent in the word *taboo* itself, which in Polynesian languages originally meant both forbidden and sacred—both cursed and consecrated.

One of the reasons sophisticated moderners look to Science is because of its reputation for not recognizing any walls. Science, we tend to imagine, roams freely over the landscape of reality, investigating everything from coyote shit to quasars. Nothing is off limits.

Religions have their truths and their heresies. You're allowed inside the church walls as long as you don't say the wrong thing, like "Gee, look at these dinosaur fossils." But Science, we imagine, welcomes all evidence.

Day Trip

Watch a TedTalk, like Michael Shermer's "Why People Believe Weird Things," and you might be convinced that Shermer has spent enough time behind the walls of the paranormal ghetto to justify slapping a big "Bullshit" sign on the whole neighborhood. Like many skeptics, Shermer gives the impression he's presenting a complete overview of the whole silly and sordid topic. The founder of *Skeptic* magazine, he's a fun tour guide, speaking with a brisk confidence and cracking jokes along the way, like, "Talking to the dead, it turns out, is easy. The hard part is getting the dead to talk back." Shermer starts by showing the audience the eight-hundred-dollar "Quadro 2000 Dowser Rod," which the Quadro corporation tried to convince high school administrators would allow them to discover weed in student lockers. Shermer points out that it's a piece of plastic with a Radio Shack antenna attached. When the laughter has died down, he goes on to show us a photograph he took of a Buick hubcap in flight and a crop circle created by Photoshop, both to demonstrate how easy it is to fake evidence. He ends his talk with a series of examples of the human susceptibility to visual and auditory illusions: We're programmed to find faces in tree bark, grilled cheese sandwiches, or church windows, as well as to hear words in random sounds such as song vocals played backwards.

Everything Shermer says is true. The Quadro corporation is scamming schools, photos can be faked, and people keen to believe are often fooled by illusions.

The trouble is that so much else is true.

Reality is big. I don't know if you've noticed. So humans bite off little pieces of it. We have no choice. The collection of little pieces we bite off is what we call our experience. Generally, anything beyond what we can imagine happening based on that experience, we deem not real.

But we usually go further than that. We tend to congregate with other people who agree with us. We read books by authors who tend to agree with us, subscribe to publications that tend to agree with us, and visit websites that tend to agree with us. All of these people, books, magazines, and websites have great recommendations for still more sources of information that tend to agree with us. Without realizing it, our world becomes a kind of pacing in an enclosure filled with people and facts fundamentally in line with our own experience. But we don't realize we're pacing. Like a fishbowl, the enclosure's walls are both invisible and smooth. It feels like we're moving freely because we keep finding out more information. But it's all the same *kind* of information.

Where could Michael Shermer have gone for a different kind of information than what he usually shares with his audiences? Where else might he have led them in the paranormal ghetto? Who else might he have talked to? And in how much depth?

Digging Deeper

Shermer might have spoken with Ricky Sorrells of Stephenville, Texas. In his book *Fringe-ology: How I Tried to Explain Away the Unexplainable–and Couldn't*, mainstream journalist Steve Volk did just that. Volk describes Sorrells as "a big, quiet man, and Texas Central cool—meaning he kept to himself, he took care of his family, and he never caused trouble." Try to put yourself in Ricky's shoes. You're out deer hunting one day. You get tripped up in the underbrush and look up as you steady yourself. Suddenly, there, three hundred feet above you, is the gray underside of some kind of aircraft so huge you can see no end in any direction. Your heart races but you try to remain calm. It dawns on you the craft is completely silent. You force your mind to slow down so you can study it. A series of inverted cones goes up a short distance into the smooth metallic surface. There are no bolts, rivets, or seams. After a few minutes, the craft rises vertically, still silent, and then leaves so fast that, as Sorrells put it, "If there is a word for that kind of speed, I haven't heard it."

Unlike the Quadro Corporation, Ricky wasn't trying to make money. Unlike Shermer, he is not on the lecture circuit giving entertaining presentations. Ricky just wants to know what happened that day. As he put it in his Texan drawl, "I used to think that people…[who] came on camera and said this kind of stuff… I thought, man, these guys need some help. You know? But it happened to me. And I can't change that. I had a hard time dealing with it."

Part of the reason Sorrells had a hard time dealing with his experience is that the culture has a hard time dealing with it. There's no respectable forum that honors it in both its psychological and physical fullness. Initially it's tempting to write it off as a hallucination. One problem with this theory is that dozens of other inhabitants of Stephenville, Texas also saw a huge craft in the sky in the days surrounding Ricky's encounter in January of 2008. Witnesses, including a private pilot named Steve Allen, described it as half a mile wide and about a mile long. Another problem with this theory is that FAA radar later confirmed the flight of an unidentified object over Stephenville.

Skeptic Michael Shermer might also have visited the Ariel School in rural Zimbabwe in the days after December 26, 1994, when more than sixty children watched a craft land some ways from their school playground during recess. Some of the children reported that the two figures who emerged communicated telepathically to them a message about the importance of caring for the earth. When the children were isolated and asked to draw what they saw, the drawings matched. Thousands of Zimbabweans reported strange aerial phenomena during the days before.

Again, our culture has a hard time with something like this. The BBC did report on the events, but it was then quickly forgotten by the general public. It wasn't forgotten by the kids. Intrigued, the Pulitzer-Prize winning Harvard psychiatrist John Mack traveled to the school and conducted in-depth interviews with them. He concluded they weren't making the story up. Now even more intrigued, Mack wrote a book called *Passport to the Cosmos*. Have you heard of it?

Snoop around a little more and it's easy to see why Shermer cut short his guided tour of weirdness. Neither he nor an army of skeptics could find the time to investigate the thousands of compelling reports of phenomena that defy conventional science. The number and variety just over the past two centuries are brain-numbing.

The most compelling accounts come from those seeking not attention but just answers. Sergeant James Penniston and Airman First

Class John Burroughs still can't explain what happened in the woods just outside their US Air Force Base in Suffolk, England in December 1980. Amid widespread reports of odd lights, the two men were sent to investigate the apparent landing of a craft, which had also appeared on radar. As the men approach the lights, visible through the trees, the air becomes still and filled with static electricity. It becomes hard to walk. An "explosion of light" sends them to the ground, after which Penniston forces himself to get up and complete his assignment. He walks around and even touches a noiseless triangular craft about nine feet long and six feet high emanating light of various shifting colors. On a small notepad, he scrawls his observations, which include sketches of symbols etched on the side of the craft. Later investigation of the site reveals broken branches, high radiation levels, and three holes in the ground suggestive of a tripod structure. The local English police respond later, noting in their log, "We have found a place where a craft of some sort seems to have landed."

Sergeant Penniston may be looking for answers. But explore more accounts, and "answers" starts to feel like a concept that just doesn't apply. In 1930, in Mandurah, Western Australia, a creature "pink like a baby," a foot and a half tall, glistening as though covered in oil, with big ears, a wide slit mouth, and bulging eyes, appears in the Hickey house. Terrified and believing it to be a demon, the religious Mr. Hickey throws a prawning net over it and drags it outside, to the creature's frightened squeaks. In Voltana, Spain, two hundred and forty locals and a couple of visiting Englishmen, see a wingless woman in white flying around overhead on at least five occasions in June of 1905. Mrs. E. E. Loznaya's flying entity, seen in 1936 in the Pavlodar region of Kazakhstan, seems to be a man dressed in black clothes that cover him completely "like overalls." He has a helmet-like head and massive square arms tightly fixed to his body. Other flying entities have bat-like wings or wings that are strapped to their bodies by a harness. Driving near Winchester, England, in November 1976, Joyce Bowles and Ted Pratt watch as a six-foot tall being passes through the side of an orange craft, approaches their parked car, places a hand on the roof, and peers inside. He has long blonde hair, a dark beard, a pale complexion, and solid pink eyes that seem to emit light. In May of 1960, Don Miguel Timermans Ceballos is motorcycling in Cadiz, Spain when he sees a six to seven-foot-tall, entirely red "Michelin Man" walking stiffly on the side of the road. After a moment, a second being appears, identical to the first, except it is about four feet tall and wears a single black boot. Eberto Villafañe is sleeping on some sheepskins at his cousin's mica mine in Cerro del Valle, Argentina one night in 1953, when he wakes up to see a beautiful woman in a tight-fitting, green, elastic-mesh garment approaching. Her feet look like serpent's heads, with eyes on the insteps. Though she motions for him to stay, he declines. While fleeing, he looks back to see her settle down on the sheepskins, which he later finds have turned yellow, as though singed. Other beings also beckon witnesses. Some approach or follow, some move quickly away. Some show no interest one way or another. Still others seem to be engaged in some activity, such as fixing their spacecraft.

There are tens of thousands of such accounts, often corroborated by multiple, independent witnesses. Since 1950 in the UK alone, the Ministry of Defense received 10,000 UFO reports, "not just lights in the sky but structured craft, sometimes tracked on radar." Air Force generals, state governors, astronauts, military and commercial pilots, police officers, deer hunters, postal workers, housewives, even Jimmy Carter and Ronald Reagan—have all reported a teeming mythology of inexplicable experiences, including encounters not only with other-worldly flying craft, but with unearthly beings, unconventional creatures, elegant designs in crop fields, and precise bloodless incisions in livestock, as well as voices, visions, visitations, ESP, and premonitory dreams.

A significant portion of peoples' accounts are bolstered by some form of physical evidence. Radar screens show objects near a pilot who reports a craft; radioactivity levels are higher or burn marks are found near supposed landing sites; witnesses suffer observable physical ailments; photographs or videos are judged authentic by special effects experts.

Multiple Witnesses

The depth and complexity of experiences like those I've just described get lost in the brevity of my descriptions. Each deserves its own book to document not just the experiences, but often their aftermaths. Their life is in their detail. Just like your life. You are not an abstraction. Whereas scientific laws are. Whether the force is applied by a horse or a hammer, force equals mass times acceleration. Similarly, Science says that one electron is exactly the same as any other electron. Skeptics like Michael Shermer often treat their human subjects like a single mass of electrons. In the absence of deep involvement with the particular experiences of unique people, skeptics offer vague abstraction that masquerades as sophistication. Shermer, for example, strongly implies that all those who report strange phenomena can be thought of as "Farmer Bob from Puckerbrush, Kansas." Then, after displaying two phony photographs, he concludes that "while it's possible... that some of [these phenomena] are real, it's more likely that all of them are fake."

Given the number and robustness of first-hand accounts, this statement is as baffling as the accounts themselves. It also suggests that Shermer believes his capacity to assess the experience of someone he's never met is more reliable than the person who had the experience. Compare Shermer's statement to one of Sergeant Penniston's after his experience in the English forest: "What I've witnessed defies all that I ever imagined... No one can fully understand such an event unless you were there." Or to the statement of another witness named Mike Sacks:

If only I could make you believe what I saw. It was there. I know it. There is not the slightest bit of doubt whatever. UFOs are real. UFOs are solid, physical craft. Nobody could possibly convince me otherwise after what I saw that night. It is just terrible *knowing* this, and yet being unable to prove it.

Now compare Sacks's statement to one of Mahatma Gandhi's, whom you may be surprised to learn received guidance from a voice "as unmistakable as a human voice definitely speaking to me." The skeptic, said Gandhi, "is free to say that it was all self-delusion or hallucination... But I can say this, that not the unanimous verdict of the whole world against me could shake me from the belief that what I heard was the true Voice of God." In the early fifteenth century, an unknown French peasant girl named Joan was also guided by something she considered heavenly. Joan's angels inspired her to travel to the royal court, where she convinced a king to put her at the head of an army, after which she turned the tide of the Hundred

Years War in France's favor. Eckhart Tolle's spiritual awakening included a distinct voice that advised, "Resist nothing."

All the West's major religions are founded around fantastic visions and impossible events—Moses before the burning bush, Jesus healing the sick and raising the dead, Mohammad's visitations from the angel Gabriel. The apostle Paul was converted by a vision of Christ, the emperor Constantine by a vision of a cross. Both men subsequently played crucial roles in the success of Christianity. University of Pennsylvania anthropologist Anthony Wallace studied hundreds of what he called revitalization movements, which he defined as "deliberate, organized, conscious effort[s] by members of a society to construct a more satisfying culture." Wallace wrote, "With a few exceptions, every religious revitalization movement with which I am acquainted has been originally conceived in one or several hallucinatory visions by a single individual."

Polytheistic cultures worldwide have also recognized not-quite-human, not-solely-physical beings that shared their existence. Whether interpreted as gods, spirits, or ancestors, they may be the single most ubiquitous feature of pre-modern belief systems. The Ojibwa called them the Memegwesi, the Japanese the Yokai, and the pre-Islamic Arabians the Jinn. Hawaiians called them the Menehune, Mayans the Ikal, West Africans the Ijiméré, and Germans the kobolds. The Germans were not alone in the West. Borderland beings flitted and burst through every pre-Medieval Western culture—pagan, Jewish, early Christian, Gnostic, and Roman. The most well-known in the English-speaking world are the Celtic Sidhe, also known as the Gentry, the Little People, the Wee Folk, the Hill Folk, the Good Folk, the Fair Folk, or just fairies.

Researcher Janet Bord writes that "anyone who thinks fairies are a joke will be very surprised to learn how many first-hand sighting reports are in existence." T.C. Kermode was a member of parliament on the Isle of Man in 1910 when he recounted how forty years earlier, walking in the country with a friend, the two saw a circle of light in a small field, into which "a great crowd of little beings" came in twos and threes, dressed in red, like soldiers. As with UFOs, sightings of fairies are often associated with lights. Dancing is also frequently reported. Like other strange beings, they come in various sizes, from "no bigger than a Coke bottle" to human-sized, though they're usually about two, three, or four feet tall. Their garb varies as well. They've been seen in "gaily-colored short skirts, their legs bare," "dressed in brown," in "bright clothes," in "a sleeveless jerkin, with tight-fitting trousers," in "shawls, and white dresses," "green from the waist down and wearing a red cap," in "a brown smock tied round the waist with a cord," "all in green," "wearing blue dungarees and a very white shirt," or "a collarless black coat buttoned up to his chin," "a bright red coat," or "in loose tunics and small, pointed hats," among other outfits.

The demeanor and complexion of fairies also vary. They have "radiant faces," or they are "sallow in complexion with long, dark bedraggled hair." Some have beards. One was "a small hairy man;" one "was bare but had a leathery look. The nose seemed sharp." Though they are known for their beauty, the one dressed all in green had "a very ugly brown face." Another "had a flat face and curly brown whiskers… from ear to ear." A woman who lay down in the woods found tangled in her hair a being about nine inches long: "the most dreadfully ugly, dreadfully misshapen, most wrinkled and tiniest mannikin I have ever seen." A mother and daughter, on the other hand, were delighted to find in their rosebush, "a little figure about six inches high, in the perfect shape of a woman and with brilliantly coloured diaphanous wings resembling those of a dragonfly."

That's Not Music

In his learned book, *Daimonic Reality*, Patrick Harpur writes that,

> No one who reviews the evidence for, say, UFOs for an hour is likely to deny that *something* strange is being seen. The trouble is, few people who have been brought up with strict rationalistic principles *can* concentrate on anomalous phenomena for an hour. They are like classically trained musicians who cannot listen to pop songs.

There's a way in which we're all classically trained musicians. As you may have noticed, reading descriptions of what we call aliens or fairies feels exhausting. The mind glazes over.

It isn't just, or even mostly, that the accounts are so strange. It's that they're so chaotic. They refuse to resolve themselves into any rule or pattern. They vary not only in detail but in feel. Some are disturbing, some wondrous, some comical, some trivial, some a mix. The mind wants to classify, conclude, or at least label. But it can't. It seems the only generalization we can make about them is that they resist generalization. They are not a cloud of electrons. Denied the activities it's so used to, the brain freezes up. If we, or someone we love, has not been personally affected by a supernatural experience, then it makes perfect sense to avoid a headache and file the lot under "Farmer Bob from Puckerbrush, Kansas." Then we can go make a sandwich.

This dismissive approach—or lack of approach—is the one mainstream science has chosen. And, often, enforced. If you don't want to get ahead in academia, take a UFO witness like Mick Sacks at his word: "It was there. I know it. There is not the slightest bit of doubt whatever." Just wanting to know more can make your colleagues' hackles rise. Author James McClenon made this mistake as a PhD candidate at the University of Maryland. As part of his dissertation in sociology, McClenon mailed a questionnaire about ESP to elite members of the Association of the Advancement of Science. Five or six of them were so vexed that they wrote letters urging McClenon be kicked out of graduate school. Others returned the questionnaire with agitated notes in the margin, one of which read, "I feel like you're trying to hurt us." McClenon said it was depressing for a fledgling sociologist, but that he was "at the same time a bit thrilled. It seemed like I was putting my finger on some kind of strange nerve." Even Pulitzer-Prize-winning Harvard professors are not immune from suspicion should they indulge heretical forms of curiosity. John Mack—the psychiatrist who interviewed the Zimbabwean school children—so disturbed some colleagues that they questioned his continued suitability as a professor. After an investigation, Mack was allowed to keep his job. It's intriguing to note exactly what the institution of Harvard chooses to investigate.

Many scientists undoubtedly censor *themselves* before their careers can suffer from an abundance of open-mindedness. We'll never know how often that happens. We do know that Dr. Elisabeth Kübler-Ross self-censored an entire chapter from her classic 1969 book *On Death and Dying*. An exploration of the human experience of death, the book broke new ground in our cultural awareness. But there is virtually no awareness that during the time Kübler-Ross spent with dying patients, she heard stories over and over of encounters with spirits, as well as near-death and out-of-body experiences. A little girl gave a description of a man who came to visit her which matched a dead uncle she'd never seen. A woman accurately described the doodles on a nurse's pad which she'd seen from above the nurse as she floated outside her body. The stories were so persistent and convincing that Kübler-Ross devoted the final chapter of her book to them. Then she thought better of it. The culture, Kübler-Ross decided, was ready for only so much awareness.

Other academics have been called on by their country to investigate strange phenomena more closely. Dr. J. Allen Hynek, chairman of the astronomy department at Northwestern University, was asked by the Air Force to evaluate UFO sightings in the 1950s. Initially a skeptic, Hynek was so impressed by the hundreds of accounts of credible witnesses that he founded *The Center for UFO Studies*. In the 1990s, the CIA asked statistics professor Jessica Utts to assess the evidence for psychic functioning. Utts is the author of mainstream textbooks such as *Seeing Through Statistics,* a guide to "the key concepts that educated citizens need to know about statistics," and in 2016 was elected the 111th president of The American Statistical Association, "the world's largest community of statisticians." In her 1996 paper, "An Assessment of the Evidence for Psychic Functioning," Utts writes, "Using the standards applied to any other area of science, it is concluded that psychic functioning has been well established... Arguments that these results could be due to methodological flaws in the experiments are soundly refuted." We could also add the testimony of the sixty-seven percent of adults who claimed to have had an ESP experience in a 1987 survey.

Unless you've been asked—and paid—to poke around in the paranormal, it's reasonable for mainstream scientists to ignore it and focus on any number of promising "normal" areas. But many, in the name of Science, feel it's important to go further. Instead of acknowledging that supernatural territory is immense, confusing, hard to study, and of questionable practical value, they would have us believe it doesn't exist. Alas, sigh the skeptics, as much as we yearn for it, there is no such thing as magic.

And yet, they make their case by performing a kind of sleight of hand. Stage magicians misdirect us away from the mundane and towards the amazing. Skeptics like Shermer misdirect us away from the amazing and towards the mundane. Their performances are often so brilliant, they themselves are fooled.

Look Over Here

But it's human to be misdirected *somewhere*. Reality, after all, is big. You may have noticed. This is why there are no lectures called, "Everything." Instead, every lecture, article, news story, conversation, guidebook, history book, science book, textbook, essay, or any human presentation or experience of any kind, is a selective portrait of reality—or a kind of magic act. Some things are included; many more things are left out. Our attention is directed to some things, away from others. This is a glaring and unarguable fact.

And yet we constantly forget it. Caught in the headlights of whatever's right in front of us, we tend to fall under its spell. Shermer enchants his audiences into believing they're seeing the whole realm of paranormal experiences. Works of art can have a similar effect. Immerse yourself, say, in Dylan's "Like a Rolling Stone" (or any piece of music you find compelling), and it feels like everything. But while lectures and art release you when you're done with them, other spells are more possessive. Growing up in a certain household and going to certain schools cast spells that seem to define you and your world in ways that feel absolute. Friends and philosophers, politicians and preachers, particular places and times—all contribute to a universe that feels both real and complete.

Since no one, from Plato to Einstein to Michael Shermer, has ever successfully defined what's real, it seems reasonable to grant that everyone's experience is a version of it. But complete? To say there are trillions and trillions of details and connections in the universe of which we are unaware feels like an understatement. To say there are roughly seven billion people right now having experiences different from ours is unarguable. To stop at any point in our daily routine and look around is to realize how much of even our immediate reality we weren't noticing before (the hum of the fridge, perhaps, or tension in our shoulders). And to believe scientists themselves is to acknowledge that even when we do pause, no matter how much we try to notice, there's a universe crowding around us that we simply can't notice. Our senses, after all, can detect only a tiny fraction of what Science has shown surrounds us. Invisible ultraviolet, infrared, micro-, and radio waves bombard us; billions of unsmellable molecules swirl inside our noses; and a symphony of sounds too quiet, too low, or too high is always playing around us. Tiny mites crawl through our eyebrows, a metropolis of cells bustles inside us, and 420 billion neutrinos (tiny particles emitted mostly by the sun) pass through every square inch of our skin every second.

Given all this, it seems fair to say that whatever you're experiencing—whether a lecture, a song, a book, a website, a conversation, a walk, or a chicken sandwich—more of reality is being left out than left in.

Comparatively speaking, in fact, what's left out is always almost everything.

Reams of Drivel

And yet, mainstream scientists are willing—even eager—to go to a lot of those unknown places. It's scientists themselves, after all, who told us about the infrared radiation, the molecules only our dogs can smell, and the 420 billion neutrinos. It's scientists who explored those invisible realms. They've even shown they can accept extreme weirdness.

Since the early twentieth century, in fact, physicists have accepted a kind of weirdness that's light years harder to imagine than the experience Ricky Sorrells had out deer hunting—or that anyone's even dreamed up in any novel, movie, myth, or religion. Never mind that physicists agree the entire universe was once compressed into a speck smaller than a grain of sand or that time speeds up and slows down depending on our circumstances. It's with quantum physics that things get really weird.

As physicists have looked at matter closer and closer, they've found that it stops being matter. It seems to turn into something else. The untold trillions of particles that everything is made of (there are about 50 billion trillion electrons, protons, and neutrons in a grain of salt) only sometimes *act* like particles. More fundamentally, they are not particles, but something physicists call probability waves. Nobody is sure exactly what these probability waves are, or if they even "are" in the conventional sense of that word. The waves tell us the probability a particle will appear at any given place. Which could theoretically be anywhere, because the probability wave of every particle in the universe covers the whole universe. And every particle, write physicists Brian Cox and Jeff Forshaw in their book, *The Quantum Universe*, "moves from one place to another by exploring the entire Universe simultaneously."

Is your head hurting? Go grab an aspirin. There's more. The reason you've never seen a probability wave is that whenever a human looks at one, it turns into a particle. The act of human observation seems to change the behavior of what physicists used to assume was an objective world. Your couch is really a collection of probability waves putting on a couch show just for you.

You might think that having had to accept such mind-shattering ideas in their description of reality, physicists would give the two hundred forty Spanish villagers the benefit of the doubt about the flying woman. Very often, though, they don't. Cox and Forshaw, the authors of *The Quantum Universe*, don't explicitly mention the paranormal, but they do feel the need to warn their readers away from the "reams of drivel" penned in the name of quantum physics. It's true, they write, that "cats can be both alive and dead; particles can be in two places at once; [and] everything is uncertain." But, they continue, the conclusion that "we are steeped in mystery [is] most definitely not" true.

Wait. Wait, wait, wait. Are Cox and Forshaw really saying that to be steeped in trillions upon trillions of "probability waves" that are spread across the universe and that pop up as particles when we look at them is most definitely not to be steeped in mystery? Are they so certain of this that they need the words "most definitely" before the word "not?" How did they arrive at such certainty? How is it even possible to be so certain about such a vague statement?

Cox and Forshaw's remark is as baffling as quantum physics itself. Why do some scientists—Cox and Forshaw, the ones James McClenon surveyed about ESP, John Mack's Harvard colleagues—get so put out, even venomous, when it comes to the paranormal?

Flakes

Many of them would doubtless say something you may be thinking as well. Where's the proof? If phenomena like aliens, fairies, and divine visitation are real and have been happening with such regularity for thousands of years all over the world in every culture, why don't we have real evidence?

To a scientist, real evidence is something that sticks around and allows a lot of people, preferably with PhDs, to measure it. Repeatability is at the heart of scientific proof. Repeatability over time and with different people. Fine, you saw that phenomenon in your lab, but can others see it under the same conditions? This is what scientists require of those who claim the supernatural realm is more than a big mess of hallucination and fraud.

But the supernatural realm is not cooperating. Or perhaps it's half-cooperating. Or even teasing. There is an ocean of reasons to believe UFOs, aliens, Bigfeet, angels, and ESP exist more robustly than just in the human imagination, but they all seem to shimmer on the border of admissible evidence. Some beings, for example, hang around an area long enough to generate multiple reports from witnesses with no connection to or knowledge of one another. The time period may range from a few hours to several days to months. In Clenendin, West Virginia, a "mothman" was reported by various witnesses from November 1966 through December 1967. The hovering, merging, darting orbs of variously colored light around Marfa, Texas have been reported off and on since 1883 by white settlers and before that by Native Americans. They've never been satisfactorily explained. (Such orbs are reported worldwide as well.) Physical evidence has frequently been attested to by reputable, official sources such as military personnel or police officers, but it has a tendency to go missing. Among numerous purported "fairy objects," one of the more intriguing is the two and seven-eighths-inch long shoe found by a shepherd on a remote sheep path in Ireland in 1835. Minutely crafted with tiny stitches, and well-worn through use, it was passed along to a local doctor and then to author Edith Sommerville. Sommerville had it examined by scientists at Harvard, who thought it likely made of mouse skin. A photo exists, but the shoe's whereabouts are now unknown. The physical evidence that does stick around usually consists not of objects but of indications of objects.

In the case of UFOs, we may get compelling photographs or videos, radar screens pinging, higher radiation levels at purported landing sites, or odd burn marks on witnesses. But we never get the craft itself. In the case of, say, Bigfoot, we get the photographs and videos and perhaps suggestively large, deep footprints, but never the creature itself.

Aliens, fairies, Bigfoot, spirits of the dead, and angels are all, it seems, united by their refusal to be pinned down. No encounter with the mothman, the Marfa lights, or any other supernatural being, has ever been booked in advance. This puts them fundamentally at odds with the scientific enterprise. The repeatability requirement at the heart of the scientific notion of reality means that scientists demand the very thing our supernatural neighbors refuse to provide: consistency.

Proof & Revelation

For a scientist, reality, by definition, is consistent. Gravity doesn't stop working when you're upset or apply only to feminists. The technology that rests on scientific truths is also dependable and universal. Computers don't disappear into thin air or only work for Republicans. Nuclear missiles can be used by both the U.S. and North Korea. The same chair will hold up Nelson Mandela or Joseph Stalin.

Couches, and other dependable features of reality, are compelling. After all, we notice them constantly. Other things, like our thoughts, feelings, dreams, and intuitions, come and go. Every day, I sit on my couch to write. But it's not every day that inspiration visits me on that couch. It's easy, then, to believe the couch is real and inspiration isn't exactly. It's easy to think that only the consistent is real.

But where is the proof that only the consistent is real?

It's hard to imagine it *could* be proven. It seems more like what's called a postulate in math. Postulates (also called axioms) are statements which can't be proven but that appear so obvious they are accepted as true. We can't prove it, but it's hard to argue with a postulate like Euclid's, "Through any two points, there is exactly one line." Postulates are used to prove more complex statements, which are used to prove even more complex statements, and so on. Postu-

lates form the foundation of the mansion—both useful and beautiful—that is modern mathematics. We could call them assumptions.

But they feel more compelling than that.

Revelations feel the same way. Nobody who experiences one requires proof. And, like the postulates of math, the revelations of
Moses, Jesus, Mohammed, Joan of Arc, Gandhi, Handsome Lake,
Joseph Smith, and hundreds of other cultural figures, have formed
the foundations of great richness—not in the form of logical systems, but of cultural transformations. The idea that only consistent
things are real—that postulate of Science—is like another useful revelation: both unprovable and felt not to require proof. By this rea-
soning, scientists are like members of a church—at least when it
comes to their notions of what's ultimately real. And like some members of some churches, some scientists attack competing revelations
with the fervor of fundamentalists.

Say What?

Ralph Waldo Emerson got the opposite memo from God. "With
consistency," he wrote, "a great soul has simply nothing to do." Emerson's vision resonates with Eastern spiritual traditions: To insist
on consistency is to miss what's *most* real. It is to substitute expecta-
tion for experience, or the "corpse of your memory" for the "thousand-eyed present."

But Emerson never had to build a parking structure. We grant
poets and artists a license to say these kinds of things. They refer,
after all, only to the shadowy world of our inner lives. In this subjective world of feeling, imagination, art, and dreams, I am free to
say that monkeys can fly and then turn into avocados, without caus-
ing scientists any discomfort. For scientists draw a line—or, we
could say, they imagine a wall—between the subjective and the objective. Most of us do.

Supernatural beings, it would seem, do not.

In their inconsistency, they resemble art and dreams. But unlike
art and dreams, they don't stay where they're supposed to—in the
subjective realm. With their multiple, perfectly sane—even embar-
rassed—witnesses, and their imprints on photographs and radar
screens, they barge into the objective world, where Science is sup-

posed to rule. Then they leave that world. When scientists demand they come back to be interrogated, they decline.

This leaves scientists either dismissive, angry, or just at a loss. A scientific law of fairies can't say they appear when they feel like it. Science needs a consistent rule, or better, an equation. Encounters with fairies can be as delightful, unsettling, or life-changing as you want. But for a scientist, to say fairies appear unpredictably to different people at different times in different guises and leave nothing behind that can be consistently tested is to say… nothing. And scientists are not Buddhist monks.

They have to say something.

Great Concept

No scientist to my knowledge has ever gotten tenure without saying something. And the thing they all say something about is human experience. This is obvious. And most of us, including many of our most brilliant scientists, also think it's obvious that all this saying something about our experience accurately reflects our *actual* experience.

But does it? How is saying something about experience connected to experience itself?

You are experiencing your immediate reality right now. But what if I ask you to say something about it? The request introduces an artificial element, like an imposition on reality. You'd probably just as soon have your experience without having to come up with a report on it. But what if I insisted, and you were feeling polite? What would you say? Well, your mind is thinking; you have various bodily sensations such as pressure on your butt; noises are coming and going; a messy sea of visual images, perhaps with some movement, lies before you; and all of this is soaking in some background mood or feeling. How to *report* on this experience? Is there any string of words, or numbers, or ideas that could capture it all or even a part of it with anything approaching accuracy or completeness?

The notion is absurd. Words, concepts, and numbers exist *within* our experience; they could never *be* that experience. They are only ever a bay leaf in the stew of sights, sounds, sensations, thoughts, feelings, bodily awareness, and temperature that we live in. That stew is fundamentally unified and indescribable. It is… what it is. To say something *about* it, I have to start choosing only certain features of it. Then I have to refer to those features with an abstraction, like a word or number. I have to isolate a hair-thin slice of my experience and then label it with a concept. Scientists, of course, have to do the same thing.

How do we choose our slices and our concepts?

I could choose the visual slice immediately in front of me. If I were on automatic mode, I might tell you I see a chair and a desk and some books and a window. But if I were to pay more attention and try to be as accurate as possible, I would need a lot more words. For I'm really seeing something incredibly complex—a kind of jungle of shadow, light, colors, curving lines, and corners. The chair's outline actually gets lost in that jungle in some places. To say, simply, that I see "a chair" is to sacrifice accuracy for generalization. It is to ignore most of my actual visual experience and substitute instead the memorized concept, "chair."

This automatic, simplistic, conceptual reporting is of course normal. It's what we all do all the time. It's how we communicate, whether we're talking to a friend or writing a physics textbook. As the poet and philosopher Owen Barfield has noted, "Outside proper nouns, every word in every language is a generalization." Numbers are even more abstract. But how else are we supposed to communicate? Our concepts save us the time of constantly re-describing that object we'd like our spouse to grab and bring over to the table.

Concepts are convenient.

But how fundamental are concepts to actual reality? Are they really out there in *what is*?

Convenient Lines

It's tempting to say, yes. At least a lot of the time. Which means it's tempting to think that scientific concepts that have proven useful are also actual, bedrock features of reality. Isn't my chair, for example, really out there as an immutable fact? And by finding its boundaries, isn't my conceptualizing mind just helping me register it as that fact? Isn't that what Science does?

Imagine, though, you're a tribeswoman from a time before chairs existed and you looked at what we call a chair. Now you wouldn't see a chair because you wouldn't have the concept of a chair. You might instead see some pieces of wood, stuck together in an odd but uninteresting way. You might think those pieces would be convenient for starting a fire. I see one chair. The tribeswoman sees fourteen pieces of kindling.

The tribeswoman would draw different boundaries within the same perception, as though walling off different elements from one another. These walls would be based on *her* concepts, which in turn would be based on her experience and needs. Like me, she would impose her own convenient ideas onto her perception.

Science philosopher Thomas Kuhn noted something similar: "Scientific fact and theory are not categorically separable." We're used to thinking that scientists meet naked facts and then come up with theories to fit those facts. But the reverse is also true. Theories *cause facts* which fit the theories—just as my "theory" of a chair causes me to find the "fact" of a chair out there in front of me.

Could it be that to see the world according to the concepts of Science—or any other concepts—is to chop up our experience in a particular way and then to call the chopped-up pieces real? What of concepts besides "chair?"

Everything we talk about, whether it's an object or an idea, we treat as though it exists within a boundary. My chair is not the desk behind it; a painting isn't the wall around it; Colorado isn't Kansas; Chemistry is not physics; velocity is not acceleration; Love is not hate; I am not you; and the subjective is not the objective. We believe they're all separate. Scientists tend to believe in separation too.

But is there even a single objective boundary that humans couldn't change or that doesn't disappear on closer examination? Chairs can be broken into kindling. State borders can be redrawn. Chemistry bleeds into physics (as well as biology). Zoom in on the most precise line you can draw on a page or computer screen and you can see its blurred and irregular edges. Under a powerful microscope, a razor's edge becomes a row of crooked teeth. At high enough magnification, in fact, the edges of all objects become a skyline of atoms. The edges of those atoms then dissolve into electrons, protons, and neutrons. And examined even more closely, according to quantum physics, those three particles become waves with no boundaries whatsoever. Quantum physics also suggests that even the boundary between the objective and the subjective is fuzzier than we think. Remember those probability waves that become particles when we look at them? Even a human being can't exactly be outlined. Your consciousness has no obvious borders and your body constantly bleeds its atoms into its surroundings, while incorporating new ones from potatoes and pork chops.

If you want to smoke weed hassle-free, you're interested in the boundary between Colorado and Kansas. If you're driving across country with your kids, you might not even notice it. If you're building a parking structure, you're interested in the boundary around a steel beam. If you're building a molecule, you need to draw some smaller lines. The only place boundaries seem to firmly exist is in our minds.

We impose walls on reality for the sake of convenience.

Science's great distinction from other human endeavors may not after all be its capacity to confront our experience in all its nakedness. It may instead be its capacity to find useful concepts. Which is to say, to build convenient walls.

Put Out

And oh, what convenience! The helpful boundaries and consistent laws scientists have discovered have made possible the helpful technology we consistently count on all day, every day—the electricity coursing through wires to our homes, the microchips in our computers, the air-conditioned comfort of our cars. By focusing on convenient aspects of reality, scientists have given us convenient lives. A person living alone could now go through their whole life without ever leaving their apartment. Business can be conducted online; food, water, and toilet paper can be delivered to our door; and waste can be whisked away through our pipes. That discipline whose job it is to confront nature has made it possible to almost completely ignore her. No culture in the history of the world has risen to such heights of convenience.

And no culture in the history of the world has so walled itself off from what is inconvenient. This might explain why no culture in the history of the world has ever so denied the existence of the supernatural. For if science is the king of the convenient, the supernatural is the queen of the inconvenient.

And not just inconvenient for scientists. It seems that almost everyone who experiences the "other world" in an immediate way is put out and confused by it. Recall the words of Ricky Sorrells, the Texan deer hunter: "It happened to me. And I can't change that. I had a hard time dealing with it." Or those of Mike Sacks: "It is just terrible *knowing* this, and yet being unable to prove it." Air Force Sergeant Penniston has had health issues since his encounter, and if that wasn't bad enough, the military won't release his medical records. Psychiatrist John Mack had to undergo an official questioning of his sanity by colleagues. Joan of Arc had to adjust from cleaning stables to leading soldiers. The supernatural is not interested in business as usual.

The supernatural, the paranormal, the "other world"—there's not even a fitting name for it. They all feel not quite right. Just like the evidence that's not quite there, and the photos that are not quite clear. No concept seems to work. Even those of us who try to write from a distance about these phenomena get turned upside down. I've never been so frustrated trying to organize an essay as I have been with this one. The supernatural inconveniences everyone who gets near it.

So why would you want to?

You wouldn't. Unless, perhaps, you were looking for God.

Something More

Historically, people have only inconvenienced themselves when they were looking for a connection to the divine. Hair shirts, worn by Christian monks or anyone seeking the spiritual realm, were inconvenient. So are the pilgrimages practiced in all religions. So is fasting during Ramadan or interrupting some aspect of your routine during Lent. So were the trips boys in tribal cultures took alone into the wild seeking the visions that would initiate them into their unique manhood. So was Alex Honnold's ropeless, four-hour climb up the face of El Capitan. If the walls we build in reality are the result of habit and convenience, people have always recognized the need to periodically transcend, break, or slide through those walls in order to access the one thing Science has failed to deliver to our doorstep: meaning.

Those in every culture who have broken their convenient routines in search of God may be inviting an experience like those enchanting ones we all have, big and small. The ones that lift us—for a moment or a lifetime—beyond the walls we'd been living behind. The fox on the path, the sunrise, the heart attack, the birth of a child, John Lennon hearing Elvis Presley, meeting your future husband at a barbecue, the apostle Paul seeing Christ on the road to Damascus. Indeed, every person's life can be seen as a series of airlifts beyond their walls—from the castle of childhood to the bigger castles of adolescence, young adulthood, and on and on.

Yes, we need walls. The cook needs a pot. The painter needs a canvas. Religions need moral codes. And Science needs consistency. We need the literal walls of our buildings and containers, and we need the metaphorical walls of our concepts. But we need more. Call it meaning or call it God. We all feel it, but no one can define it. Maybe that's because the "more" that we need is "more" itself. More love, more life, more of ourselves, more of whatever's beyond the walls we've been pacing within.

Perhaps aliens, fairies, Bigfoots, voices, and visions visit us to remind us of that "more." Perhaps they are versions of tricksters, those boundary-busting shaker-uppers of the status quo that have always bobbed and weaved through the myths of almost every culture on the planet. "The mind structures a lifestyle," wrote Joseph Campbell, "and the… trickster represents another whole range of possibilities." If this is so, then to embrace these strange phenomena as our neighbors is not to probe them for answers—not to decide once and for all what they are or are not. For answers are stopping places. Answers are walls.

We're so used to walls—so used to taking them seriously. But these phenomena subvert the idea of any barrier. Like reality itself, they present as walls but are really doors.

To meet them in the same spirit, then, would be not to stop at them and debate what they really are. Or even to experience them or read accounts of them. To truly embrace them may be to walk *through* them to embrace an idea that is un-embraceable, or that requires constant re-embracing—the idea that there is always something beyond our ideas, beyond what we're experiencing, beyond what we can understand right now, beyond how we're used to seeing reality. Pushing us beyond our presumed limits, such visitations can't help but often be unsettling—even, sometimes, terrifying. But maybe anything is only terrifying to the extent that we're insisting on concepts that don't apply—or banging our heads against walls that aren't really there.

V. The Science Spell
Science & the Big Picture

"Unless you expect the unexpected, you will never find truth."
—*Heraclitus*

I recently listened to Larry King interview the astrophysicist and science guru Neil deGrasse Tyson. Larry asked Neil what he thought happened to us after we die. Tyson began his response by saying, "Well, I can make some unassailable statements about what happens when you die." He then explained how the food we eat contains chemicals with energy, how we use that energy to function, and how when we die, we don't maintain the energy any longer. If we're cremated, it radiates into space as heat; if we're buried, worms and microbes get it. Tyson, in other words, seems to believe what I used to believe. Death is the eternal extinction of consciousness.

Eternal. That's *forever* for the layperson. No snacks, no bathroom breaks, no parole hearing after 45 trillion years. Tyson seems to be OK with that. As long as he's buried. He loves the idea of bequeathing his chemicals to worms. Sounds like a hoot, Neil.

But Tyson is convincing. He speaks with confidence and vitality. He's a master teacher. Being a master teacher is like being a master storyteller. Or a master songwriter, painter, novelist, philosopher, political theorist, or preacher. To be a master in any of these realms is to create a compelling world.

Worlds

Every human lives in a world. Not *the* world, but a world. And usually whatever world we're in feels compelling. An office is a compelling world. When you go to work, you enter a physical, emotional, intellectual "space" where certain rules, expectations, and activities exist, and where certain things are considered of utmost importance. Everyone and everything around you seems to reinforce this. Meanwhile, a farmer gets up and enters a completely different world. A third-grade teacher enters yet another.

But it's more complex than a simple "one-person-equals-one world" equation. For most of us move into different worlds as we go through our life and even our day. When we leave work, we enter a new world—the subway, say. Here, a sales manager is suddenly stripped of his authority. His suit and tie now mark him not as someone to be feared but as someone who fears. The rulers in this world wear ripped jeans and backward baseball caps. When we come home from work, we enter yet another world. Different rules apply, different expectations. Rear Admiral George Morrison had a military career that included the command of U.S. naval forces in the Gulf of Tonkin when the 1964 incident there kicked the Vietnam war into high gear. At home, he faced a different kind of trouble: his teenage son, the future rock star Jim Morrison. Which was more of a challenge—the Viet Cong or Jim—is hard to say, but each was certainly part of a different world for George.

But the physical place you're in isn't the only—or even the most important—factor in creating your world. Every person that comes into that office on Wednesday morning is in their own particular variation of the "Office World." They carry their ideas about life and themselves and other people with them. Patrick is shy because he constantly expects to get criticized by all the parents... uh, *co-workers* around him. Gloria is loud and gets in everybody's face because she knows you gotta call it like you see it. Both Patrick and Gloria walk around in the same office but are in largely different worlds. Both are experiencing different results from the way they are in that world.

Now add to this complexity the fact that we're always changing, in big and small ways. We grow up from little kids to adolescents to teens to young adults and so on. We learn, adapt, or get more and more entrenched. So even if we remain in the same physical place, we still change our world by experiencing that place differently. A student who has a wilderness adventure in the Sierras the summer after junior year comes back to high school with new eyes. She notices new things, thinks of herself differently, perhaps with more confidence. The world of high school has changed.

Now add the worlds of other species living right alongside us—say, your dog. There she is right next to you in the living room, but occupying a radically different world—one filled with high-pitched sounds you can't hear, awash in myriad odors you can't smell, and apparently suffused with a kind of unconditional love that few humans maintain for long.

Spells

Worlds overlap, co-exist, pop, blend, and change all the time. You could even say that every instant is a new world. Yet it's easy to get sucked into a certain world or a certain version of a world and believe it's fundamentally, absolutely real. A world is a spell. There could be all sorts of things around you, but you only notice what the spell allows you to notice.

Growing up with a certain personality, in a certain place, with certain parents can cast a spell on you. Mentors, friends, schools, books, experiences, or jobs can all cast spells on you. Religions, philosophies, and political theories can cast spells on you. Spells are self-reinforcing. You begin to see the world according to the ideas that compel you. You read more books along the same lines, seek out people, experiences, facts, and statistics that contribute to the spell.

It's easy to notice the nature of the spells that others are in. You can clearly see that your friend Maya occupies a simplistic world in which, say, all men are liars. Or that your colleague Anthony lives in a world where some people will be raptured and others won't. Lots of us can point out the strange features of the worlds our least favorite politicians seem to inhabit. We don't as readily acknowledge the spell-like nature of our own worlds. That feels too disorienting. After all, we've built our lives around our spells.

Often, we allow a work of art to cast its spell on us. The greater the work of art, the more powerful a spell it casts. Accuracy or truth doesn't enter into it—at least in the factual sense. We can be transported to a compelling world by a great Dylan song, like "Visions of Johanna," or "Like a Rolling Stone." We can stand entranced before a Rembrandt portrait. We can be completely immersed in the waters of a good novel. Art, though, respects your autonomy. It holds you only as long as you let it. You're aware of your control over the spell—that you can turn off the song, look at a different painting, close the book.

When you "leave" a work of art, you break its spell. You can then reflect on that spell and gain perspective. Our power to break the spell of art is an important element in our experience of art. Horror movies cast a terrifying spell, but surely people go to them in part because there's a greater comfort in the awareness that it's "just a movie." When it's over—or even before that—we can cross the threshold of the theater doors, look up at the sky or over at the Target across the parking lot, and feel held by something larger than the movie world.

All art is generous in this way. Every work offers us not only a new world to explore, but also clearly displays that world's exit signs. We get to be held by the art and also aware that we hold the art. When it comes to the world of a work of art, in other words, we're more aware of that world's boundaries.

Boundaries

Imagine living in the old days—in medieval Europe or a tribal society. Back then, the idea of "something" beyond the boundaries of your known physical world was easy to picture. There were actual physical limits to where anyone had been. You could stand on the shore, say, of the Atlantic Ocean and look out over that immense sheet of water and wonder what was out there. Or you could look up at the blinking stars and wonder what on earth they were. No one had ever been across the sea or out into space. No one had even dug down into the ground beneath you more than a few score feet. You could feel yourself surrounded—maybe embraced—by a very immediate mystery. What was out there, up there, down there—*there,* where you were pointing? What was beyond your world?

There had to be something. So, based on your experiences in your world, you imagined that something. Your myths—or religion—populated that realm with beings. They were like you, but more powerful and more permanent. Something grand was going on just across the boundaries of your immediate world—just outside the movie theater you were in.

You could imagine yourself cradled by that "something"—like a child held in a mother's arms. When the ancient Greeks looked far enough west across the sea, they stopped picturing more regular old hills and people, and saw the entrance to Hades. When the Blackfoot looked at the moon, they didn't think "big rock" like we do, but *Ko'komiki'somm*, second eldest of the Sky People, wife of the sun god *Naato'si*, mother of the stars. When a medieval peasant looked up into the same night sky, she didn't experience an empty abyss, but concentric spheres filled with angels and ultimately God. Stop for a moment and feel what that would be like: to every night look up and feel the presence of angels—*real* angels—surrounding you.

The Swiss missionary and anthropologist Hans Shärer, who lived with the Dayak people of Borneo for seven years, left us a sense for what it feels like to be held in this way:

> The Dayak loves the world into which he is born and where he grows up. His village is the largest and most beautiful place in the whole world and he would change it for no other… Why roam far among strangers? Peace, safety, happiness, and the good life are to be found only in one's own village—only in one's own world, where one is protected by the godhead, surrounded by the primevally maternal water snake, where one rests on its body and is enclosed by its head and tail.

Meaning

Something unquenchable—some "fire inside"—burns in us. It's an insistence that we somehow matter—deeply. It's a need to be eternal or part of something eternal. Call it a sense of grandeur, wonder, love, or meaning. Whatever we call it, the ancients had a place to "put" it: out there, across the boundaries of their world, where they could physically point every day.

We don't have that now. While there are places "out there" we haven't been, we believe we know what they're like. We've mapped the entire planet. We know there's no Purgatory beyond the sea—just more dirt, plants, animals, and people who blow their noses like we do. We know there's no space beyond the sky filled with gods and angels, just our endless modern "space," filled with billions of nuclear furnaces and chunks of inert matter.

But the fire inside still burns. We still want meaning. We still look for it. Even Neil deGrasse Tyson looks for meaning in his impersonal scientific vision of the universe—that delight he claims to take in the idea of passing along his body to worms and microbes.

As far as inspirational ideas go, however, getting munched on by grubs isn't quite in the same league as gods, angels, and eternal bliss. Say what you will about those old beliefs, they answered something in the human soul. Well-meaning scientists like Tyson do their darndest to make their subject soul-stirring, but it's like putting lipstick on a horrible, eternal void. Not a good look for a void.

That void's grin has been widening for centuries now, in our art, our philosophy, and our lives. It's that vague sense of meaninglessness under everything, that emptiness in the core, that blank of death waiting. You could feel it under Larry King's question for Tyson. Larry was really saying, "You're a smart guy, Neil. So help me. Please. Help me alleviate this terror that's buzzing in the background of everything I do, this thing we all live with, but are too polite to scream about."

Neil answered Larry's superficial question with confidence and flair. But he had nothing for Larry's deeper question. *Nobody* smart seems to have anything for Larry's deeper question. All the smart people believe in Science.

No Boundaries

And why shouldn't they? Isn't Science our oracle? Doesn't it keep answering our questions about reality? Hasn't it given us endless conveniences and toys, from microwaves, planes, nuclear power plants, computers, iPhones, and the internet, to video games, theme parks, Las Vegas, and 64 oz. sodas? Neil deGrasse Tyson isn't on Larry King just because he's a compelling personality. He's also there because he's backed up by thousands of experiments, technologies, textbooks, and universities.

This is all to say that if you have the modern viewpoint for which Tyson speaks, you see the world Science offers as qualitatively different from those other worlds created by religions, philosophies, works of art, your workplace, or your parents. Those are "worlds" with air quotes. But Science World is official. To view the world scientifically, we believe, is to snap out of all the spells. We're seeing things as they are—mechanical. No matter where we work or how we were raised, we're all made of chemicals, all registering vibrations of air molecules as sounds, and so on. Science defines the *actual* world that contains all those metaphorical ones. Science is that ultimate thing beyond or under the nice ideas and metaphors that we make up. Science isn't *a* world. It's *the* world.

More than that, it's the universe. It's everything. And there are no boundaries to everything. We can travel as far as we want now, even in our imagination, but we can never leave the movie theater.

Fruits & Thorns

It can seem like a package deal. The iPhones, planes, and microwaves come with the endless void. They are not sold separately. Every world, in fact—Patrick's, the medieval peasant's, the scientist's—is a kind of bargain. Every world serves us and hurts us in different ways. Shy Patrick keeps to himself at work to avoid the criticism that his world is ready to rain down on him should he make a mistake. That criticism could be crippling. In order then to function at all, it makes sense for Patrick to lay low as much as possible. So what if he doesn't get the promotions. He likes his paycheck. The medieval peasant may not have loved working till her back was stiff, sleeping next to a cow, or never having a bath, but we can assume that heaven sounded mighty good, and, life expectancies being what they were, not too far away.

We tend to believe the world we're in—or the spell we're under—is the only possible one for us, and so we also tend to accept it, warts and all. We muddle through. We eat its fruits and live with its thorns. The fruits of "Science World" are amazing. They are also fleeting. But the thorns are eternal. Science reverses the medieval

peasant's bargain. The Church gave the peasant a tedious life in return for a dazzling after-life. Science gives us a dazzling life in return
for an after-life that's the ultimate snooze-fest.

Solid & Shaky

To believe Science offers us *the* world is to believe it's fundamental.
Finally, we think, we're getting down to brass tacks. Finally we're
walking on solid ground.

You could say the ancients walked on shaky ground. For they
stood on a mystery. Literally. They also stood within a mystery. Mystery was under, over, and around them. Into that unknowable realm,
they poured their innate need for magic and meaning. Then they felt
it washing back over them.

How did that make them feel?

It seems to have made them feel at home in the universe. So
much so that they felt they *were* the universe—or at least a partici-
pating element, as much as a lion, a mountain, the wind, or a flower
was. Yes, they made up stories about the universe. But their stories
weren't hard-and-fast rational explanations of things. Rather, they
were myths.

To our modern ears, myths seem like explanations—but really
lame ones. "We got fire when Prometheus stole it from Zeus? Um.
OK," we say, "So now I've got, like, a million questions about that."
In what seems like a paradox to us, myths were explanations that
didn't end mystery, but rather channeled it. Myths gave answers that
weren't rational but resonant. Humans felt themselves as partici-
pants in a grand tale. In this state of being—under this kind of
spell—it didn't occur to people to ask what the world was made of,
what's ultimately true, what we're doing here, or any of the other
questions that plague us today.

People in cultures across Asia and Europe only started asking
the kinds of existential questions we'd now call *philosophical* during
what's been called the Axial Age, between about 800 and 400 B.C.E.,
when a shift in consciousness seems to have occurred. In our Western tradition, the Axial Age was kicked off by the pre-Socratic
Greeks around 600 B.C.E. For a long time after this, the old mythic
sensibility co-existed alongside the newer analytic attitude. During

the Scientific Revolution, though—starting roughly with Copernicus around 1540—the analytic approach started building up steam. That's the steam we live in today.

But our longing for magic, mystery, and meaning hasn't gone away. Every child is born with it. All kids look out at the world expecting it, imagining it, creating it. Tell them a jolly man in a red suit flies through the air in a sleigh pulled by reindeer one night a year distributing gifts to every boy and girl in the world, and they believe it—quite matter-of-factly. It's not a stretch for them because expecting that kind of magic comes with being human. Children feel something dazzling in themselves or in the world—it's hard to tell the difference. They dream about it. They see it in unicorns and superheroes.

In our culture, though, that innate need doesn't have a surrounding space to flow out to, fill, and then come washing back over us. Instead, it smashes up against the cold hard "reality" of Science. We don't have a name for that smashing. But it hurts. Continually. We feel it in the thud of a dream deflated. We feel it in the space after someone we love dies and leaves us, so it seems, forever. We feel it in that nameless anxiety that clutches the throat. It's the sadness in the background as we watch our kids grow up and move towards the inevitable. It's the silent scream in Munch's painting—and in Larry King's question for Neil deGrasse Tyson.

Paradoxically, that solid, absolute, fundamental ground that Science seems to offer makes us feel wobbly at our core. The ancients walked on shaky myths and felt solid. We walk on solid Science and feel shaky.

Science Ground

But how solid, really, is the ground of Science?

Neil deGrasse Tyson, along with many other smart-sounding people, certainly sounds like he's walking on solid ground when he uses scientific words, like "chemicals," in his conversations about the possibility of some kind of after-life—as though the word, or concept, of "chemicals" was bedrock. As though we couldn't dig into it.

In a way, this makes perfect sense. The word "chemicals" sounds official, after all. It's in lots of textbooks and it explains lots of things. In fact, the word "chemicals" probably sounds as official to modern ears as the words "The Bible" sounded to medieval ears. And one doesn't question official-sounding words. One doesn't dig into the ground one walks on. Right?

Actually, a lot of people do. We just don't hear their words as often as we hear all those official-sounding ones. Physicists, for example, have been probing what chemicals are made of since the turn of the twentieth century.

And what they've found is beyond weird. When we dig into the world "beneath" chemicals, where the rules of quantum physics reign, our words no longer seem to apply. Concepts we take for granted—like time, particle, wave, matter, energy, location, observer vs. thing observed, cause-and-effect, and even the categories of existence or non-existence—often blend or just become irrelevant. This "ultimate reality" physicists have discovered is arguably stranger than those crazy ultimate realities our ancestors imagined— whether it's Prometheus stealing fire from Zeus or the earth sitting on the back of a turtle.

But it's not just the word "chemicals" that smart people tend not to investigate. Smart people—people with PhDs, people who go on talk shows, people who publish books filled with data—walk around on all kinds of words which they leave sitting there as if they were definite, as if we all agreed on what they were, as if it were even possible to agree on what they were. As if, in other words, they were walking on solid ground.

In fact, with just a little digging we find that almost all the bed-rock words Science habitually walks around on start to fall apart and evaporate. Like Wiley Coyote, if we look down at them, we fall right through them. We toss around the word "reality," for example, as if anyone has come close to a definition of it. We blithely believe that Science is based on "evidence," and "experience," without acknowledging that Science doesn't count most of our experience as evidence, because most of it can't be repeated in controlled lab conditions. Without offering proof for why it should be true, mainstream Science rests on the idea that phenomena are only real when they repeat themselves in ways we can predict.

It isn't just certain kinds of phenomena scientists aren't interested in. There are whole realms of human experience that mainstream scientists don't recognize as valid and therefore don't explore with anything approaching the resources they devote to, say, physics or chemistry. Throughout history, in every culture, and continuing unabated today, countless thousands of normal, smart, skeptical people have had experiences that current science cannot explain. Visitations, visions, voices, and dreams have started religions and changed people's lives. In response, skeptics generally hold up for exhibit the instances where a "strange" phenomenon turns out to be either natural or fraudulent, while ignoring the tens of thousands of other compelling reports, often from multiple, independent witnesses or bolstered by some form of physical trace.

Deemed impossible by scientific institutions, such phenomena exist in a blind spot in the official Western view of the world. We've never heard, for example, of Bhagawan Nityananda of Ganeshpuri, India—who died in 1961 after a lifetime marked by the simplest living and providing for the poor—even though countless eyewitnesses tell stories of his healing, clairvoyant, and other miraculous powers. We don't know that Dr. J. Allen Hynek, PhD, chairman of the astronomy department at Northwestern University, was asked by the Air Force to evaluate UFO sightings in the 1950s and was so impressed by the hundreds of accounts of credible witnesses that he founded *The Center for UFO Studies*. We don't learn in Psychology 101 that "psychic functioning has been well established," with results "far beyond what is expected by chance," according to a prominent professor of statistics who was tapped by the CIA to assess the available evidence. Nor do we learn in Biology 101 of the evidence gathered from two studies that some humans, like Indian holy man Prahlad Jani, may not need to eat, drink, or pass waste. We're unaware that for her classic book, *On Death and Dying*, Elisabeth Kübler-Ross originally wrote a final chapter about the compelling testimony of her dying patients concerning encounters with spirits—in some cases, accurately describing dead relatives they'd never met—and out-of-body experiences (She decided to drop the chapter so that the rest of her book would be taken seriously.) I know a woman whose out-of-body experiences as a child were such a matter of course that she thought they were part of being human—until she started realizing they were "weird." But despite the similar experiences of multitudes, the official scientific view that consciousness arises only from a brain remains unshaken. Jeffrey Kripal, a Professor of Philosophy and Religious Thought at Rice University sums up the bigger picture that mainstream scientists often don't take in: "If we collect enough seemingly anecdotal or anomalous experiences from different times and places and place them together on a fair comparative table, we can quickly see that these reports are neither anecdotal nor anomalous. We can see that they are actually common occurrences in the species."

Practically Miraculous

It turns out, there *are* boundaries to what seems like the official world of Science, just as there are boundaries to any other world. Amazingly too, it doesn't take—if you'll excuse the expression—a rocket scientist to find them. In fact, the kind of focus that people like rocket scientists need to do their job requires them *not* to explore those boundaries. In the words of the particle physicists and co-authors Brian Cox and Jeff Forshaw, "The ability not to ask too many questions is a necessary skill in physics... in order to answer any questions at all."

But those boundaries become apparent when we simply ask some childlike questions, without regard for their social acceptability or convenience. If we're made of chemicals, what are the chemicals made of? If your thought is just a nerve impulse, what caused the nerve impulse? Why do you believe your five senses give you a complete picture of reality when quantum physics tells us every object is really a collection of trillions of probability waves, each one spread across the universe? How do you explain the wingless woman in white seen flying overhead in Voltana, Spain by two hundred and forty locals and a couple of visiting Englishmen, on at least five occasions in June of 1905? What are the darting, merging, elusive orbs of light that have been reported for decades around Marfa, Texas and in other places around the world, witnessed by all manner of people, including scientists? In his non-fiction book, *Travels,* why did Michael Crichton claim he saw silverware get all rubbery at a spoon-bending party?

Like an office or a movie theater, there's something bigger outside Science—a greater dimension. Last I heard in fact, cutting-edge theoretical physicists were proposing eleven dimensions to explain reality. I have a feeling that number is going to grow. And grow. And grow. Perhaps the ancients just cut to the chase: mystery and magic are inevitable—they are the world beyond whatever world we're in. They are always just beyond the boundaries of whatever we know.

Science is that world in which we think there are no more worlds. It's a world where we think we need to throw a wet blanket on that fire inside us—where we finally need to stop all that nonsense and "get real." Science is a myth that thinks it has put an end to myths. Science is a myth that doesn't know it's a myth.

How did we fall under this spell?

The same way we fall under any spell—only multiplied by a million. Spells work because they seem to surround us, and because they encourage us to think, feel, and act in ways that reinforce them. The spell of Science does this in spades. But most of all, like a good spell, Science serves us. Big time. Nothing I've said here is to deny its usefulness. And that's just it. Science is the most dazzling spell of all because it's so damned practical. In fact, it's practically miraculous.

That phrase, "practically miraculous," is true twice.

First, Science is miraculous in a practical way. It seems able to solve any practical problem. Thus the spell. If Science can do all that, surely it can do everything. Surely there are no other gods, no other worlds. And so we come to Science wanting it to solve the deepest problems of all, like children who come to their mother's breast wanting the sweetest milk of all.

But Science's breasts—and I'm truly sorry for that image—are dry. Science is our modern Great Mother, minus the milk. For Science is also "practically miraculous" in the sense that it isn't *fully* miraculous. It has nothing to say about that inextinguishable spark in your soul—the sense that you are so much bigger than any endless void.

If you enjoyed this book,
please leave a review on Amazon.
Thank you.

Acknowledgments

Thank you to my editor, Taylor Ray, whose keen eye, clear head, and kind words made me dig deeper and made these essays better.

Thank you to Tina Koenig for helping to guide this book into the daylight with her care, experience, and attention to detail.

Thank you to Guita Naeima for allowing my writing to marry the exquisite dreams of her art.

Thank you to my sister, Sarah, who has always walked beside me.

About the Author

Born in rural New Hampshire, Chris Spark (a.k.a. Chris Dingman) graduated *summa cum laude* with a BA in Biology from Harvard, where he was vice-president of *The Harvard Lampoon*. While an undergraduate, he also began writing poetry and exploring myth, spirituality, and his own psyche.

Since then, he has taught science and math, optioned a comedy screenplay to Warner Bros.—among other adventures in Hollywood—learned the guitar, started a band, and recorded three CDs of original songs. More recently, after way too much psychotherapy, Spark has returned to poetry and philosophy.

One of Chris's pieces was included, alongside those of John Updike and Conan O'Brien, in *The Best of the Harvard Lampoon: 140 Years of American Humor*. He is also a contributor to *The American Bystander*, which *Newsweek* called "the last great humor magazine."

Chris's books of poems include *The Trees Sing Hallelujah, This Dreaming World, Advice for Me and Maybe You,* and *Haiku Wisdom: 101 Daily Morsels for the Spirit.*

This book is Volume 1 in Spark's series, *Making Belief: Essays towards a Natural, Magical, Intelligent Faith.* Volume 2 is *Of Geometry & Jesus: Essays from Outside the Fishbowl of Western Culture.*

His books are available wherever books are sold and at:

www.SparkWrites.com

Notes

Introduction

1. **"the beginning of happiness"**: George Santayana 1910, *Three Philosophical Poets: Lucretius, Dante, and Goethe*, Chapter V: Conclusion (Project Gutenberg version) https://www.gutenberg.org/files/35612/35612-h/35612-h.htm)

I. The Science Fiction

1. **"nobody would notice"**: Cormac McCarthy 2010, *Cities of the Plain*, cited at Goodreads.com, "Cormac McCarthy quotes." Available at https://www.goodreads.com/author/quotes/4178.Cormac_McCarthy?page=10
2. **"apparently reabsorbed by his bladder walls"**: Rajeev Khanna 2003, "Fasting fakir flummoxes physicians," *BBC News*, November 25. Available at http://news.bbc.co.uk/2/hi/south_asia/3236118.stm (Accessed May 20, 2020)
3. **"something that's not supposed to happen"**: "Man survives without food, water for 65 yrs" 2010, *News 18*, April 29, https://www.news18.com/videos/india/yogi-study-337519.html (Accessed May 20, 2020)

4. **"to observe Jani for a longer period: fifteen days":** Adam Halliday 2010, "DRDO watching man who hasn't eaten in '70 yrs'" *The Indian Express,* April 28. Available at http://archive.indianexpress.com/news/drdo-watching-man-who-hasnt-eaten-in-70-yrs/612181/1 (Accessed May 20, 2020)

5. **"healthier than someone half his age:"** Tom Rawstorne 2010, "The man who says he hasn't eaten or drunk for 70 years: Why are eminent doctors taking him seriously?" *Daily Mail*, May 7. Available at https://www.dailymail.co.uk/news/article-127477 9/The-man-says-eaten-drunk-70-years-Why-eminent-doctors-taking-seriously.html (Accessed May 20, 2020)

6. **"The complete history of science has to be written anew":** P.A. Straubinger, "Prahlad Jani." *Light Documentary.* Available at https://www.lightdocumentary.com/prahlad-jani.html (Accessed May 20, 2020)

7. **"who has said he would welcome it":** 2010, "Mataji to go under international scanner," *Daily Bhaskar,* September 14. Available at https://daily.bhaskar.com/news/mataji-to-go-under-international-scanner-1363591.html (Accessed May 20, 2020)

8. **"VanRooyen told the reporter, you'd die of kidney failure":** Brian Alexander 2010, "70 years without eating? 'Starving Yogi' says it's true," *NBC News*, May 10. Available at https://www.nbcnews.com/healthmain/70-years-without-eating-starving-yogi-says-its-true-1C9926692 (Accessed 23 May 2020)

9. **"Jani was "setting himself up for nutritional deficiencies":** Karen Russo 2010, "Scientists Baffled by Prahlad Jani, Man Who Doesn't Eat or Drink," *ABC News*, May 31. Available at https://abcnews.go.com/Health/International/man-eat-drink/story?id=10787036 (Accessed May 20, 2020)

10. **"even in serious journals, are pretty sloppy":** Ivan Couronne 2015, "Beware those scientific studies—most are wrong researcher warns," July 5, *Phys.Org.* Available at https://phys.org/news/2018-07-beware-scientific-studiesmost-wrong.html (Accessed May 20, 2020)

11. **"may often simply be accurate measures of the prevailing bias":** John P. A. Ioannidis 2005, "Why Most Published Research Findings Are False," August 30. https://doi.org/10. 137 1/journal.pmed.0020124

12. **"More than one in ten scientists report seeing this behavior in their peers"**: Daniele Fanelli 2009, "How Many Scientists Fabricate and Falsify Research? A Systematic Review and Meta-Analysis of Survey Data," May 29. https://doi.org/10.1371/journal.pone.0005738

13. **"He is unable to explain the accuracy of others"**: Michael Crichton 2015, *Travels* [Audiobook Version], (Brilliance Audio), Chapter 21, 00:06:34 – 00:19:11

14. **"more interested in seeing what kinds of cookies they had"**: Crichton 2015, Chapter 34, 00:00:09 – 00:04:20

15. **"I had bent a spoon, and I *knew* it wasn't a trick"**: Crichton 2015, Chapter 34, 00:04:50

16. **"it seemed to require a focused inattention"**: Crichton 2015, Chapter 34, 00:05:37

17. **"We've just forgotten we can do them"**: Crichton 2015, Chapter 34, 00:09:13

18. **"*Travels* was published in 1988"**: 'Michael Crichton,' Wikipedia, Wikimedia Foundation, May 17, 2020. https://en.wikipedia.org/wiki/Michael_Crichton (Accessed May 20, 2020)

19. **"be taken seriously in her field or tell the entire truth"**: Steve Volk 2011, *Fringe-ology: How I Tried to Explain Away the Unexplainable—and Couldn't*, (HarperOne), pp. 28-32.

20. **"important psychological studies of the late twentieth century"**: according to Amazon description of the hardcover, Scribner Classics edition (1997) of the book. Available at https://www.amazon.com/Death-Dying-Elisabeth-K%C3%BCbler-Ross-ebook/dp/B0053GIJFO/ref=sr_1_1?crid=3FRVFSQAVS64B&dchild=1&keywords=on+death+and+dying+by+elizabeth+kubler-ross&qid=1590077694&s=books&sprefix=on+death+%2Caps%2C240&sr=1-1. (Accessed May 20, 2020)

21. **"to know how to face ridicule"**: Miguel de Unamuno 1954, *The Tragic Sense of Life*, translated by J. E. Crawford Flitch, (Dover Publications), Kindle version, location 4904.

22. **"to have visions or hear voices"**: Helen Castor 2015, *Joan of Arc: A History* [Audiobook] (Tantor Audio), Chapter 1, 00:10:28

23. **"a passionately popular war of national liberation"**: Stephen Richey 2000, "Joan of Arc: A Military Appreciation," stjoan-center.com, Available at http://www.stjoan-center.com/military/stephenr.html (Accessed April 2, 2020)

24. **"have no such dark implications":** Oliver Sacks 2012, *Hallucinations* [Audiobook Version] (Random House Audio), Introduction, 00:11:50

25. **"and had the courage to testify":** *Intervoice* 17 May 2011, "Famous People." https://www.intervoiceonline.org/voices/famous-people. (Accessed June 6, 2020)

26. **"are actually common occurrences in the species":** Whitley Streiber and Jeffrey J. Kripal 2017, *The Super Natural: Why the Unexplainable is Real* (Tarcher Perigee), p. 81

27. **"Resist nothing":** Eckhart Tolle 2000, *The Power of Now* [Audiobook] (New World Library), Introduction, 0:03:14.

28. **"hallucinatory visions by a single individual":** Anthony F. C. Wallace 1956, "Revitalization Movements," *American Anthropologist* 58: 264-281. https://doi.org/10.1525/aa.1956.58.2.02a00040

29. **"what I heard was the true Voice of God":** Mahatma Gandhi, *Intervoice* (May 17, 2011). http://www.intervoiceonline.org/2494/voices/famous-people/mahatma-gandhi.html (Accessed May 20, 2020)

30. **"received a visit from the Inquisition":** F. Mershman 1910, "St. Joseph of Cupertino. *The Catholic Encyclopedia* (Robert Appleton Company), Available at New Advent: http://www.newadvent.org/cathen/08520b.htm

31. **"under oath by over a hundred and fifty eyewitnesses":** Michael Grosso 2015, "Evidence for St. Joseph of Copertino's Levitations," Esalen.org. Available at https://www.esalen.org/sites/default/files/resource_attachments/Ch-1-Supp-Joseph.pdf (Accessed May 21, 2020)

32. **"among the earliest to receive these wounds":** Mike Dash 2011, "The Mystery of the Five Wounds," *Smithsonian Magazine*, November 18. Available at https://www.smithsonianmag.com/history/the-mystery-of-the-five-wounds-361799/ (Accessed May 21, 2020)

33. **"during a vision of a six-winged seraph on a cross":** Lawrence Cunningham and Ignatius Charles Brady 2018, "St. Francis of Assisi," *Encyclopædia Britannica* (Encyclopædia Britannica, Inc.) December 2, Available at https://www.britannica.com/biography/Saint-Francis-of-Assisi (Accessed May 21, 2020)

34. **"the simplest living, providing for the poor"**: Swami Muktananda 1996, *Bhagawan Nityananda of Ganeshpuri* (Siddha Yoga Publications; 2nd edition)

35. **"the poet William Blake saw angels"**: see for example, Peter Ackroyd 1996, *Blake: A Biography* (Alfred A. Knopf)

36. **"Carl Jung conversed with a spirit guide"**: see for example, "Who is Philemon?" *Philemon Foundation*, https://philemon-foundation.org/about-philemon/who-is-philemon/ (Accessed May 21, 2020)

37. **"through spiritual practices, meditation, drugs, or solitude"**: Sacks 2012, Introduction, 00:11:25

38. **"scientific boundaries are not created by philosophical argument"**: James McClenon 1994, *Wondrous Events: Foundations of Religious Belief* (University of Pennsylvania Press), p. xiii

39. **"to investigate extremely far-fetched theories"**: Ibid, p. 3

40. **"scared of things which seem to be outside that reality"**: Michael Swords, Interview. David Cherniak Productions Ltd. Available at http://www.allinonefilms.com/html_pages/UFOs_Swords.htm (Accessed Dec. 17, 2020)

41. **"subversive of its basic commitments"**: Thomans Kuhn 2012, *The Structure of Scientific Revolutions*, Fourth edition (University of Chicago Press), p. 5

42. **"A little brainwashing will go a long way"**: Paul Feyerabend 2010, *Against Method*, Fourth edition (Verso), p. 3.

43. **"putting my finger on some kind of strange nerve"**: James McClenon, "Parapsychology as a deviant science with James McClenon," *New Thinking Allowed With Jeffrey Mishlove* [Video]. YouTube. December 21 2018, https://www.youtube.com/watch?v=UWw_ll2dTs8 (Accessed May 21, 2020)

44. **"ideological fanaticism of many of the skeptics"**: Volk 2011, pp. 64-65.

45. **"might be of considerable interest to psychologists" (and preceding quotations)**: J. Allen Hynek 2017, *The UFO Experience: A Scientific Inquiry* [Kindle Edition], pp. 8 – 14 (originally published 1972, Da Capo Press)

46. **"remote viewing 'works with remarkable precision'"**: "Coordinate Remote Viewing (CRV) Technology 1981 – 1983" 1983, CIA Briefing, *CIA* August 4, p. 3. Available at https://

www.cia.gov/library/readingroom/docs/CIA-RDP96-00788R001100520001-3.pdf (Accessed May 10, 2020)

47. **"sources throughout the DoD intelligence community":** "Project Stargate," CIA Document, *CIA*. Approved for release August 8, 2000. p. 36. Available at https://www.cia.gov/library /readingroom/docs/CIA-RDP96-00789R003300210001-2.pdf (Accessed May 10, 2020)

48. **"can be developed to a person's potential":** Ibid., p. 10

49. **"largely ignored in today's societal setting":** Ibid., p. 10

50. **"you haven't had much practice,' says the Queen back":** Lewis Carroll 1991, *Through the Looking Glass* (The Project Gutenberg Ebook), Chapter V. Wool and Water

51. **"textbooks such as *Seeing Through Statistics*":** Jessica Utts 2016, "Home Page for Jessica Utts Department of Statistics University of California, Irvine," *UCI Donald Bren School of Information and Computer Sciences*, Available at https://www.ics.uci.edu/~j utts/ (Accessed May 22, 2020)

52. **"educated citizens need to know about statistics":** according to Amazon description of the paperback, Cengage 4th edition (2014) of the book. *Amazon*. Available at https://www.amazon. com/Seeing-Through-Statistics-Jessica-Utts/dp/1285050886 (Accessed May 22, 2020)

53. **"the world's largest community of statisticians":** "About" page, *American Statistical Association*, amstat.org. https://www. amstat.org/ASA/about/home.aspx?hkey=6a706b5c-e60b-496 b-b0c6-195c953ffdbc (Accessed May 22, 2020)

54. **"flaws in the experiments are soundly refuted":** Jessica Utts 1995, "An Assessment of the Evidence for Psychic Functioning," *Donald Bren School of Information and Computer Sciences, University of California, Irvine* https://www.ics.uci.edu/~jutts/air.pdf (Accessed May 9, 2020)

55. **"illnesses that doctors deemed irreversible":** see for example, Caryle Hirschberg and Brendan O'Regan 1993, *Spontaneous Remission: An Annotated Bibliography* (Institute of Noetic Sciences), as described at https://library.noetic.org/library/publication-bibliographies/spontaneous-remission (Accessed May 22, 2020)

56. **"which is normally used to *induce* vomiting":** "Placebo treatment for pregnant women," *Placebo-world.com*, Available at http://www.placebo-world.com/nausea.php (Accessed May 22,

2020). (This is a summary of Stewart Wolf 1959, "The Pharmacology of Placebos," *Pharmacological Reviews* 11 (4), 689 - 704, http://pharmrev.aspetjournals.org/content/11/4/689.full.pdf+html

57. **"as effective as actual surgery":** Baylor College Of Medicine 2002, "Study Finds Common Knee Surgery No Better Than Placebo." *ScienceDaily* July 12. www.sciencedaily.com/releases/2002/07/020712075415.htm (Accessed May 23, 2020)

58. **"or in whole via the placebo effect":** Alia J. Crum and Ellen J. Langer 2007, "Mind-set matters: Exercise and the placebo effect," *Psychological Science* 18 (2): 165-171. http://nrs.harvard.edu/urn-3:HUL.InstRepos:3196007

59. **"the mind can heal the body":** Lissa Rankin, MD 2012, "Is there scientific proof we can heal ourselves?" *TEDxAmericanRiviera* [Video]. Youtube. Dec. 18. 00:00:32 https://www.youtube.com/watch?v=LWQfe__fNbs (Accessed May 23, 2020)

60. **"an inconvenient truth":** Ibid., 00:00:49

61. **"become as little children":** Matthew 18:3, *King James Bible*

62. **"wise as serpents and innocent as doves":** Matthew 10:16, conflation of translations from *King James Bible* and *New International Version*.

II. Who Should We Ask About God?

1. **"The world and I are within one another":** Maurice Merleau Ponty 1968, *The Visible and the Invisible*, Translated by Alphonso Lingis and edited by Claude Lefort (Northwestern University Press) p. 123

2. **"Why should I live?":** Stephen Pinker 2018, *Enlightenment Now: The Case for Reason, Science, Humanism, and Progress* [Audiobook] (Penguin Audio), Opening Credits, 00:03:30 – 00:03:45.

3. **"until I find the ones that don't":** This quote is widely attributed to Edison (see, for example, https://edisonian.weebly.com/quotes.html, or www.thoughtco.com/edison-quotes-1991614), but its source is unconfirmed. Other similar statements at-

tributed to Edison include: "Negative results are just what I'm after. They are just as valuable to me as positive results," quoted by The Library of Congress at https://www.loc.gov/collections/edison-company-motion-pictures-and-sound-recordings/articles-and-essays/biography/life-of-thomas-alva-edison/

4. **"when the need for illusion is deep":** Saul Bellow 1976, *To Jerusalem and Back: A Personal Account* (Penguin Books), p. 127

5. **"according to a 2014 survey":** Christopher Ingraham 2014, "Study: Americans are as likely to believe in Bigfoot as in the big bang theory," *The Washington Post*, October 24. https://www.washingtonpost.com/news/wonk/wp/2014/10/24/study-democrats-are-more-likely-than-republicans-to-believe-in-fortune-telling-astrology-and-ghosts/ (Accessed May 23, 2020)

6. **"It consists of the many realities that it can be made into":** Wallace Stevens 1997, *Collected Poetry & Prose* (Library of America) p. 914.

7. **"In my father's house":** John 14:2, *King James Bible*

8. **"knowledge by approximation":** Maurice Merleau-Ponty 2004, *The World of Perception* (Routledge), p. 35

9. **"believing in God is silly":** Richard Dawkins 2008, *The God Delusion* (Mariner Books)

10. **"in order to answer any questions at all":** Brian Cox and Jeff Forshaw 2011, *The Quantum Universe (and why anything that can happen, does)* (DaCapo Press), p. 97

11. **"not at all uncommon among perfectly sane people":** Oliver Sacks 2012, *Hallucinations* [Audiobook Version] (Random House Audio)

12. **"Socrates, and Mahatma Gandhi":** *Intervoice* 17 May 2011, "Famous People." https://www.intervoiceonline.org/voices/famous-people. (Accessed June 6, 2020)

13. **"what I heard was the true Voice of God":** Mahatma Gandhi, *Intervoice,* 17 May 2011. http://www.intervoiceonline.org/2494/voices/famous-people/mahatma-gandhi.html (Accessed May 20, 202)

14. **"a great soul has simply nothing to do":** Ralph Waldo Emerson 1841, "Self-Reliance," *Essays First Series.*

15. **"and by giving others what she expects for herself":** Pinker 2018, Opening Credits, 00:04:20 – 00:05:43

III. What You See Is What You See

1. **"it is the illusion of knowledge":** Daniel J. Boortsin, quoted by Carol Krucoff in "The 6 O'Clock Scholar," *The Washington Post*, January 29, 1984. Available at https://www.washingtonpost.com/archive/lifestyle/1984/01/29/the-6-oclock-scholar/eed58de4-2dcb-47d2-8947-b0817a18d8fe/ (Accessed April 21, 2020)

2. **"said the German philosopher Friedrich Nietzsche, 'is dead.'":** Friedrich Nietzsche 1882, *The Gay Science*

3. **"getting worse instead of better.":** Our World in Data, https://ourworldindata.org/wrong-about-the-world (Accessed December 2, 2019)

4. **"In 2015, 86% could.":** Stephen Pinker 2018, *Enlightenment Now: The Case for Reason, Science, Humanism, and Progress* (Penguin Random House), p. 86

5. **"since 1980 the world has also gotten 14% greener":** Zhu, Z., Piao, S., Myneni, R. et al 2016, "Greening of the Earth and its drivers," *Nature Clim Change* 6, 791–795. https://doi.org/10.1038/nclimate3004 (Accessed May 23, 2020)

6. **"has risen for 178 of the 180 countries it tracks":** Pinker 2018, p. 130

7. **"oxygen (1774)":** Ann Marie Helmenstine 2018, "Element Discovery Timeline," ThoughtCo.com, Oct. 3. https://www.thoughtco.com/element-discovery-timeline-606607 (Accessed May 23, 2020)

8. **"Nature loves to hide":** Heraclitus Fragment 123, translation cited by Daniel W. Graham, "Does Nature Love to Hide? Heraclitus B123 DK," Classical Philology 98, no. 2 (April 2003): 175-179. https://doi.org/10.1086/381371 (Accessed May 23, 2020)

9. **"a feeling for the order lying behind the appearance":** Albert Einstein 1933, Prologue to *Where is Science Going?* by Max Planck (W. W. Norton & Company)

10. **"the most successful theory in the history of science":** see, for example Graham Farmelo 2019, "A realist takes on quantum mechanics." *Nature* 568, 166-167. doi:10.1038/d41586-019-01101-0, or Adam Becker 2018, *What is Real?* (Basic Books) p. 1

11. **"billions of pieces of confirming evidence for quantum mechanics"**: Seth Lloyd 2011, "Quantum Leap." *The Fabric of the Cosmos* [TV series]. Nova. 00:06:15

12. **"lasers, transistors, magnets, and superconductors"**: Daniel F. Styer 2000, *The Strange World of Quantum Mechanics* (Cambridge University Press), p. 3

13. **"by exploring the entire Universe simultaneously"**: Brian Cox and Jeff Forshaw 2011, *The Quantum Universe (and why anything that can happen, does)* (DaCapo Press), p. 2

14. **"they could instantaneously appear anywhere"**: Ibid., p. 46

15. **"a two-dimensional hologram"**: See, for example, Jacob D. Berkenstein 2007, "Information in the Holographic Universe," *Scientific American*, April 1. Available at https://www.scientificamerican.com/article/information-in-the-holographic-univ/ (Accessed May 26, 2020)

16. **"big and small become equivalent"**: Roger Penrose, in "Before the Big Bang 7: An Eternal Cyclic Universe, CCC revisited & Twistor Theory," [Video]. YouTube. Uploaded by skydivephil 8 March 2018, 00:05:03. Available at https://www.youtube.com/watch?v=FVDJJVoTx7s (Accessed May 26, 2020)

17. **"weighs four billion tons"**: Robert Naeye, "One Weird Type of Star Acts Like Another," *NASA*, 2 January 2008. https://www.nasa.gov/topics/universe/features/whitedwarf_pulsar.html (Accessed May 23, 2020)

18. **"it was proven"**: "Spooky action at a distance" was Einstein's description of what quantum physicists call "entanglement" between two particles. It was conclusively proven to happen with photons by Alain Aspect in the early eighties, and has since been demonstrated with other particles.

19. **"420 billion per square inch per second"**: among many sources, see Clara Moskowitz 2014, "Strange Neutrinos from the Sun Detected for the First Time," *Scientific American,* Aug 27, https://www.scientificamerican.com/article/solar-neutrinos-detected-borexino/ (Accessed May 23, 2020)

20. **"these two blind spots: ninety-five percent"**: Jorge Cham and Daniel Whiteson 2017, *We Have No Idea: A Guide to the Unknown Universe* (Riverhead Books), p. 13

21. **"constant river of New Age nonsense"**: Adam Becker 2018, *What is Real?* (Basic Books) p. 281

22. **"most definitely not' true"**: Cox and Forshaw 2011, p. 4

23. **"made of the heart"**: "Yamakavagga: Pairs," *The Dhammapada*, translated by Thanissaro Bhikkhu 1997. *Dhammatalks.org*. Available at https://www.dhammatalks.org/suttas/KN/Dhp/Ch01. html (Accessed May 23, 2020)

24. **"it escapes being known"**: Heraclitus Fragment 86, as quoted by Darrell Arnold, PhD, in "Heraclitus, Fragment 86" [Heraclitus Blog], 19 June 2018, *DarrellArnold.com*. Available at https://darrellarnold.com/2018/06/19/heraclitus-fragment-86/ (Accessed May 25, 2020). Arnold quotes a translation by Andre Laks and Glen W. Most.

25. **"and it will be yours"**: Mark 11:24, *The Bible*, New International Version. Available at https://biblehub.com/mark/11-24.htm

26. **"Nothing worthy proving can be proven"**: Alfred Lord Tennyson 1885, "The Ancient Sage," *Tiresias and Other Poems*

IV. Where Scientists Fear to Tread

1. **"accept them as unalterable givens"**: Don A. Howard and Marco Giovanelli, "Einstein's Philosophy of Science", *The Stanford Encyclopedia of Philosophy* (Fall 2019 Edition), Edward Zalta (ed.) https://plato.stanford.edu/archives/fall2019/entries/einstein-philscience/, which cites Einstein in "Ernst Mach." *Physikalische Zeitschrift* 17: 101–104. Repr. in CPAE, Vol. 6, Doc. 29.

2. **"Why People Believe Weird Things"**: Michael Shermer 2006, "Why people believe weird things" [*Ted* Video]. Youtube. February. https://www.youtube.com/watch?v=8T_jwq9ph8k&t=322s (Accessed May 23, 2020)

3. **"and he never caused trouble"**: Steve Volk 2011, *Fringe-ology: How I Tried to Explain Away the Unexplainable—and Couldn't* (HarperOne), p. 113.

4. **"I haven't heard it"**: Ibid., p. 119

5. **"I had a hard time dealing with it"**: Ricky Sorrells 2015, *I Know What I Saw* [TV Documentary], Directed by James Fox:

01:09:15. Available at https://www.amazon.com/UFOTV-Pres ence-Know-What-Saw/dp/B01MRRIURA (Accessed 23 May 2020)

6. **"and about a mile long":** numerous news agencies 2008. See, for example, Wade Goodwyn (reporter) and Deborah Tedford (writer) 2008, "Dozens Claim They Spotted UFO in Texas," *NPR*, January 16. Available at https://www.npr.org/2008/01/ 16/18146244/dozens-claim-they-spotted-ufo-in-texas

7. **"an unidentified object over Stephenville":** Staff Report 2008, "MUFON says radar reports confirm UFO sightings," *Stephenville Empire-Tribune*, July 13 Available at https://www.your stephenvilletx.com/news/article_e9c944d6-ff16-54f3-8e74-8d0 87cfd7329.html. (Accessed May 23, 2020)

8. **"strange aerial phenomena during the days before":** Brian Kingsley 2019, *Unexplained Mysteries of the World* (Brian Kingsley) [Audiobook version], Chapter 4, 00:00:00 - 00:05:11. See also: "Remembering Zimbabwe's great alien invasion," 2014, *Mail & Guardian*, September 4. Available at https://mg.co.za/article/ 2014-09-04-remembering-zimbabwes-great-alien-invasion/ (Accessed May 30, 2020)

9. **"a book called *Passport to the Cosmos*":** Ibid., Chapter 4, 00:06:30

10. "etched on the side of the craft": Nick Pope with John Burroughs, USAF (Ret.), and Jim Penniston, USAF (Ret.) 2014, *Incident in Rendlesham Forest, The Inside Story of the World's Best-Documented UFO Incident*, (Thomas Dunne Books, St. Martin's Press) [Kindle version]. p. 66, location 1277

11. **"suggestive of a tripod structure":** Ibid., p. 26, location 598 (and previous)

12. **"a craft of some sort seems to have landed":** Ibid., p. 11, location 348

13. **"to the creature's frightened squeaks":** Janet and Colin Bord 1989, *Unexplained Mysteries of the Twentieth Century* (McGraw Hill) p. 147

14. **"on at least five occasions in June of 1905":** Ibid., p. 146

15. **"square arms tightly fixed to his body":** Ibid., pp. 147 – 148

16. **"solid pink eyes that seem to emit light":** Patrick Harpur 2003, *Daimonic Reality: A Field Guide to the Otherworld* (Pine Winds Press), p. 28

17. **"and wears a single black boot":** Bord 1989, p. 152
18. **"have turned yellow, as though singed":** Ibid., p. 150
19. **"sometimes tracked on radar":** Nick Pope (desk officer, UK Ministry of Defense) 2015, *I Know What I Saw*, 01:25:38
20. **"even Jimmy Carter":** Jimmy Carter 1969, "Report to the International UFO Bureau in Oklahoma City," *NICAP* (*National Investigations Committee on Aerial Phenomenon*) Available at http://www.nicap.org/waves/CarterSightingRptOct1969.pdf (Accessed May 24, 2020)
21. **"and Ronald Reagan":** The Editors of Publications International, Ltd. 2008, "Ronald Reagan Sees a UFO" *HowStuffWorks.com*, 19 February. https://science.howstuffworks.com/space/aliens-ufos/ronald-reagan-ufo.htm (Accessed May 16, 2020)
22. **"Farmer Bob from Puckerbrush, Kansas":** Shermer 2006, 00:03:32.
23. **"it's more likely that all of them are fake":** Ibid., 00:05:15
24. **"unless you were there":** Pope et al 2014, p. 11, location 348
25. **"and yet being unable to prove it":** Harpur 2003, p.11
26. **"the true Voice of God":** Mahatma Gandhi, *Intervoice,* 17 May 2011. http://www.intervoiceonline.org/2494/voices/famous-people/mahatma-gandhi.html (Accessed May 20, 202)
27. **"the Hundred Years War in France's favor":** Helen Castor 2015, *Joan of Arc: A History* [Audiobook Version] (Tantor Audio)
28. **"Resist nothing":** Eckhart Tolle 2000, *The Power of Now* [Audiobook Version] (New World Library), Introduction, 00:03:14.
29. **"one or several hallucinatory visions by a single individual":** Anthony F. C. Wallace, 1956. "Revitalization Movements," *American Anthropologist* 58: 264-281. https://doi.org/10.1525/aa.1956.58.2.02a00040
30. **"The Ojibwa called them the Memegwesi":** See, for example George Eberhart 2002, *Mysterious Creatures: A Guide to Cryptozoology* (ABC-CLIO, Inc), p. 324, or "Legendary Native American Figures: Memegwesi (Mannegishi)," *nativelanguages.org*, http://www.native-languages.org/memegwesi.htm
31. **"the Japanese the Yokai":** See, for example Keiko Hill 2019, "Japanese Monsters, Ghosts, and Spirits: Mythical Yōkai (妖怪) at OSU Libraries," University Libraries, *The Ohio State University* September 9. https://library.osu.edu/site/japanese/2019/09/

09/japanese-monsters-ghosts-and-spirits-mythical-yokai-%E5
%A6%96%E6%80%AA-at-osu-libraries/

32. **"the pre-Islamic Arabians the Jinn"**: See, for example, The Editors of Encyclopædia Britannica 2018, "Jinni," *Encyclopædia Britannica* (Encyclopædia Britannica, Inc.) November 16, Available at https://www.britannica.com/topic/jinni (Accessed May 23, 2020)

33. **"Hawaiians the Menehune"**: See, for example "The Menehune of Hawaii: Ancient Race or Fictional Fairytale?" *Ancient Origins*. Available at https://www.ancient-origins.net/myths-legends/menhune-hawaii-ancient-race-or-fictional-fairytale-001741

34. **"the Mayans the Ikal"**: Eberhart 2002, p. 245

35. **"the West Africans the Ijiméré"**: Ibid., p.245

36. **"Germans the kobolds"**: See, for example, The Editors of Encyclopædia Britannica 2019, "Kobold," *Encyclopædia Britannica* (Encyclopædia Britannica, Inc.) August 28. https://www.britannica.com/topic/kobold (Accessed May 24, 2020)

37. **"pagan, Jewish, early Christian, Gnostic, and Roman"**: Patrick Harpur 2002, *The Philosopher's Secret Fire: A History of the Imagination* (Blue Angel Gallery), p. 15

38. **"the Fair Folk, or just fairies"**: Janet Bord 2013, *Fairies: Real Encounters with the Little People* [Kindle Edition] (Michael O'Mara Books Ltd.), location 89

39. **"how many first-hand sighting reports are in existence"**: Ibid., location 51

40. **"wings resembling those of a dragonfly"**: This and previous descriptions of fairies, Ibid., Chapters 1 – 3.

41. **"who cannot listen to pop songs"**: Harpur 2003, p. xvi

42. **"some kind of strange nerve:"** James McClenon 2018, "Parapsychology as a deviant science with James McClenon," *New Thinking Allowed With Jeffrey Mishlove* [Video], YouTube, Dec. 21, https://www.youtube.com/watch?v=UWw_ll2dTs8 (Accessed May 21, 2020)

43. **"was ready for only so much awareness"**: Volk 2011, pp. 27-32

44. **"he founded *The Center for UFO Studies*"**: Greg Daugherty 2018. "Meet J. Allen Hynek, The Astronomer Who First Classified UFP 'Close Encounters," *History*, November 19. https://

www.history.com/news/j-allen-hynek-ufos-project-blue-book (Accessed May 9, 2020)

45. **"citizens need to know about statistics"**: according to Amazon description of the paperback, Cengage 4th edition (2014) of the book. Amazon. Available at https://www.amazon.com/Seeing-Through-Statistics-Jessica-Utts/dp/1285050886 (Accessed May 22, 2020)

46. **"president of The American Statistical Association"**: Jessica Utts 2016, "Home Page for Jessica Utts Department of Statistics University of California, Irvine," *UCI Donald Bren School of Information and Computer Sciences*, Available at https://www.ics.uci.edu/~jutts/ (Accessed May 22, 2020)

47. **"the world's largest community of statisticians"**: "About" page, *American Statistical Association*, amstat.org. https://www.amstat.org/ASA/about/home.aspx?hkey=6a706b5c-e60b-496b-b0c6-195c953ffdbc (Accessed May 22, 2020)

48. **"methodological flaws in the experiments are soundly refuted"**: Jessica Utts 1995, "An Assessment of the Evidence for Psychic Functioning," *Donald Bren School of Information and Computer Sciences, University of California, Irvine.* https://www.ics.uci.edu/~jutts/air.pdf

49. **"an ESP experience in a 1987 survey"**: 2014 Harvey J. Irwin and Carolyn J. Watt, *An Introduction to Parapsychology* (McFarland, fifth edition) p. 31

50. **"every square inch of our skin every second"**: among many sources, see Clara Moskowitz 2014, "Strange Neutrinos from the Sun Detected for the First Time," *Scientific American,* Aug 27, https://www.scientificamerican.com/article/solar-neutrinos-detected-borexino/

51. **"by exploring the entire Universe simultaneously"**: Brian Cox and Jeff Forshaw 2011, *The Quantum Universe (and why anything that can happen, does)* (DaCapo Press), p. 2

52. **"is most definitely not"**: Ibid., p. 4

53. **"from November 1966 through December, 1967"**: Kingsley 2019, Chapter 2: "The Mothman Cometh." See also numerous other sources, such as Krissy Howard 2017, "The Story of the Mothman, The Legendary Creature That Terrorized A West Virginia Town In The 1960s," *ATI allthatsinteresting.com.* Available at

https://allthatsinteresting.com/mothman (Accessed May 30, 2020)

54. **"(Such orbs are reported worldwide as well.)"**: Kingsley 2019, Chapter 10: "Ghost Lights." See also numerous other sources, such as Marc Lallanilla 2013, "What Are the Marfa Lights?" *Livescience.com*, June 19, https://www.livescience.com/37579-what-are-marfa-lights-texas.html (Accessed May 30, 202)

55. **"the shoe's whereabouts are now unknown"**: see Harpur 2003, pp. 134-135; or Bord 2013, location 369

56. **"for the "thousand-eyed present"**: Ralph Waldo Emerson 1841, 'Self-Reliance," *Essays, First Series.*

57. **"every word in every language is a generalization"**: Owen Barfield 1973, *Poetic Diction: A Study in Meaning* (Wesleyan University Press), p. 108

58. **"Scientific fact and theory are not categorically separable"**: Thomans Kuhn 2012, *The Structure of Scientific Revolutions,* Fourth edition (University of Chicago Press), p. 7

59. **"another whole range of possibilities"**: Joseph Campbell in *An Open Life: Joseph Campbell in conversation with Michael Toms,* selected and edited by John M. Maher and Dennie Briggs (Harper and Row, Perennial, edition 1, 1990), p. 39

V. The Science Spell

1. **"you will never find truth"**: Heraclitus, *The Complete Philosophical Fragments*, translated by William Harris, *Faculty Projects Web Archive*, Middlebury College, March 23, 2016. https://wayback.archive-it.org/6670/20160323155720/http://community.middlebury.edu/~harris/Philosophy/Heraclitus.html (Accessed May 15, 2020)

2. **"what happens when you die"**: Knowledge Initiative 2017, "Neil deGrasse Tyson getting asked by Larry King about his views on the afterlife," November 7 [Video]. YouTube. https://www.youtube.com/watch?v=QHudASQpw9I (Accessed May 18, 2020)

3. **"mother of the stars"**: Legendary Native American Figures: Ko morkis (Ko'komiki'somm). http://www.native-languages.org/komorkis.htm (Accessed May 10, 2020)

4. **"and is enclosed by its head and tail"**: Hans Shärer, as cited by Ninian Smart 2006, *The Religion of Small Societies* [Audiobook Version] (Blackstone Audio), Chapter 1, 3:50.

5. **"and other miraculous powers"**: Swami Muktananda 1996, *Bhagawan Nityananda of Ganeshpuri* (Siddha Yoga Publications)

6. **"he founded *The Center for UFO Studies*"**: Greg Daugherty 2018, "Meet J. Allen Hynek, The Astronomer Who First Classified UFP 'Close Encounters,' " November 19. https://www.history.com/news/j-allen-hynek-ufos-project-blue-book (Accessed April 23, 2020)

7. **"to assess the available evidence"**: Professor Jessica Utts 1995, "An Assessment of the Evidence for Psychic Functioning," *Donald Bren School of Information and Computer Sciences, University of California, Irvine.* Available at https://www.ics.uci.edu/~jutts/air.pdf

8. **"may not need to eat, drink, or pass waste"**: Bharat Yagnik 2019, "Super power: Thirst & a yogi," *Times of India*, April 28 https://timesofindia.indiatimes.com/city/ahmedabad/super-power-thirst-a-yogi/articleshow/69077176.cms. But see also numerous other news reports, including ABC, NBC, and the BBC, as well as the documentary film, *In the Beginning There Was Light* (https://www.lightdocumentary.com/prahlad-jani.html)

9. **"so that the rest of her book would be taken seriously"**: Steve Volk 2011, *Fringe-ology: How I Tried to Explain Away the Unexplainable—and Couldn't*, (HarperOne), pp. 28-32

10. **"they are actually common occurrences in the species"**: Whitley Streiber and Jeffrey J. Kripal 2017, *The Super Natural: Why the Unexplainable is Real* (Tarcher Perigee), p. 81

11. **"in order to answer any questions at all"**: Brian Cox and Jeff Forshaw 2011, *The Quantum Universe (and why anything that can happen, does)* (DaCapo Press), p. 97

12. **"on at least five occasions in June of 1905"**: Janet and Colin Bord 1989, *Unexplained Mysteries of the 20th Century* (McGraw Hill), p. 46

13. **"witnessed by all manner of people, including scientists"**: Ibid., p. 142

14. **"he saw silverware get all rubbery at a spoon-bending party":** Michael Crichton 1988, *Travels* [Audiobook version] (Brilliance Audio), Chapter 34, 00:00:09 – 00:04:20

Your Thoughts:

Made in United States
North Haven, CT
07 January 2025

64091926R00074